Golda Slept Here

SUAD AMIRY

women
UNLIMITED
an associate of
kali for women

Golda Slept Here
was first published in India in 2014 by

**Women Unlimited
(an associate of Kali for Women)
7/10 Sarvapriya Vihar
First Floor
New Delhi 110 016**

www.womenunlimited.net

*Published by arrangement with Feltrinelli
for sale in South Asia only*

© 2014, Suad Amiry

ISBN: 978-81-88965-81-6

Cover design: Neelima Rao

Typeset at Sanchauli Image Composer, New Delhi 110 059
Printed at Raj Press, R-3, Inderpuri, New Delhi 110 012

Contents

Part Four
Elie: A Bird's-eye View

Part Five
Homage to My Mother-in-law
1911-2005

Home

Whose house is this?
.....
Say, who owns this house?
.....
This house is strange
Its shadows lie
Say, tell me, why does its lock fit my key?

— Toni Morrison

It is in the hope of eliminating, rather than perpetuating, the dark side of humanity that I write this book.

I was told: "Home is where I am."
I try hard but I do not always succeed.

Gabi

May you rest in peace, knowing that your story will be told and retold as many times as you wanted it to be.

To Gabi Baramki who sadly passed away as I was working on this book.

To Gabi who had, over the years, shared with me and others the passion and agony of a Master Builder who happened to be his father. Like many, I have lost a beloved friend but also a close neighbour: your deep loud voice, '*Keefek ya jara*' will always stay with me. If it is any consolation, Gabi had read, approved and "loved" my version of his story.

To Andoni Baramki, Gabi's father, with the haunting, enigmatic, otherworldly smiles that never left his face.

To all the people in this book who have graciously shared with me their memories, their losses, their emotions, as well as their ever-present pain. The anguish and fear of remembering and forgetting made some of them choose not to be included in this book.

And this I *fully* understand.
The wound is still open.

To Huda al-Imam: the Joan of Arc of Palestinian memory, and
To Teta Aysheh and Baba Farid.

To Elie Sanbar, who will be utterly surprised to see his story in this book. As he passionately narrated his story, I was mentally recording every little detail of an utterly absurd situation.

And a homage to my late mother-in-law, the renowned Umm Salim.

To the 'absentees,' who constituted ninety per cent of 1948 Palestine, and who have so far not been allowed to be present.

And to the present who are considered absent
To each 'present absentee' who lives steps away from a home that has become someone else's.

And finally
To *all* and everyone who lost the pillars for a sane life
A profound foundation called HOME.

Part One

Suad: Remembering and Forgetting

Map 1: Jerusalem Suburbs

American Colony

Bab ez Zahira
Wadi el Jo

Mea Shearim

Musrara

Old City

Mamillah
Cemetery

Rehavia

Yemin
Moshe

Talbiya

El Qatamon

German & Greek Colony

Deir Abu Tur

El Wa'riya

El Baq'a

•••••••• 1948 Armistice Line

I

They Missed Mama's Cooking

Exhausted, I lay on my back in bed, waiting for my adrenaline level to drop.

The night promises to be long, very long.

With eyes wide open I gazed at the beautiful cross-vaulted ceiling of my bedroom at Rema and Alex's house. For the last twenty-some years they have been living in the gorgeous Hindiyeh family house in Sheikh Jarrah, an East Jerusalem Arab neighbourhood recently targetted by Jewish settlers.

I would like to think that both Rema and Alex were delighted to have a close friend descend on them from the other side of the Separation Wall. I cannot claim that I was fun company that evening, as the acrobatics of 'illegally' sneaking into Jerusalem with Huda's help had totally drained me. Though excited to see me, they too had committed a 'criminal offence' by giving me a bed (actually a mattress on the floor) in their lovely house.

Not that I had contemplated going to a hotel – none of the hotels in Arab Jerusalem would risk giving a room to a Palestinian without a permit – but I only hoped that the pleasure of seeing me was worth the risk that Rema and Alex were taking in hosting me for the night.

I rolled on my right side trying hard to fall asleep.

My mother's deep voice reached my ears. I could not but follow it to the house just down the road from where I was

3

lying: "Susu habibti, it is true that you were born in Damascus, but you were conceived in Jerusalem." My mother smiled as she revealed this endearing detail of my conception. I was thirty years old when she surprised me with this fact. I had left Amman by then, where she and I had been living, and come to live in Palestine. I must say having been conceived in Jerusalem was news to me – big and delightful news indeed.

Though we are *not* to imagine or visualise the act of love-making that brought us into this world, that night I did. It was an intimate and heated act. What I loved most about it was the likelihood that it followed the ecstasy of eating the yummy Zalatimo cheese pie *mtabaq* from my favourite sweet shop in the Old City of Jerusalem.

And since my brother Ayman and I were born a few years after the 1948 Nakba (catastrophe), I somehow felt that my mother had invented this maculate Jerusalem conception story:

> Every full moon, your Baba and I would drive from Amman to the Dead Sea, spend one night at the Lido Hotel and then drive back to Jerusalem the following day. We spent the mornings strolling in the narrow streets of Jerusalem, had a *mtabaq* at Zalatimo's, then spent the rest of the afternoon on the terrace of the National Hotel where we would stay the night, or drive to the Grand Hotel in Ramallah.

Hmm … to have been conceived in Jerusalem meant only one thing: my parents made love *only once* that weekend, otherwise how could my mother claim that I was conceived in Jerusalem? Why not at the Dead Sea, or even Ramallah? As lovely as it sounds, I had my suspicions. Realising how happy this would make me, my mother, like the Israelis (with a big difference in scale and purpose) had a tendency and talent to invent 'facts'.

I rolled onto my left side, trying hard to sleep.

"Born on a full moon night," Mama often told me, and she was probably right. As my parents continued to make such trips, I personally witnessed some of these full moon nights on the Dead Sea shore. But 'conceived in Jerusalem,' I'm not so sure.

One thing I do know for sure is that the house in which my newly-wed parents lived in 1942 and from which they fled in 1948 was just down the road from where I was tossing in bed in November 2011.

I also knew that the two-storey house in which they had lived belonged to the Ghosheh family. While the owners lived upstairs, my parents lived on the first floor. "I loved living in Jerusalem more than any other city, simply because the Jerusalemites were aloof and stingy," my mother always said. "And as a result, they left you in peace. Unlike Damascus, Beirut and Salt (in Jordan) where people invite you to visit and keep you under surveillance day and night, the Jerusalemites couldn't be bothered, and hence never interfered in anyone's business."

Another virtue of my mother's, in addition to fabricating facts, was that she never praised someone without also pointing out his or her bad points. She applied the French *jolie-laide* (beautiful-ugly) to everything in her life, including the Jerusalemites whom she adored. "I loved all my neighbours in Jerusalem, especially Umm Samir Ghosheh with whom I had a barter relationship. I would bring her and her three daughters red lipstick and other make-up from Suq al-Hamidiyeh in Damascus. In return she prepared for me platters of stuffed squash, stuffed grape leaves, stuffed potatoes, stuffed tomatoes, stuffed onions, stuffed peppers and stuffed cabbage. Of all the varieties of *mahashi* (stuffed vegetables) what I liked best were the stuffed purple carrots. They were so tough to core that Umm Samir had to send them to a carpenter in the Old City to drill holes in them."

Spending so much time stuffing everything that lent itself to filling or rolling in any way or form, I am not surprised that the

5

Jerusalemites never had the time to raise their heads or look out of their windows to see what their neighbours were up to.

Having a rich Syrian uncle, Jamil Far'oun, who owned a lovely house in the Talbiyeh neighbourhood and many businesses, including Abdo Taxi Company that travelled between Jerusalem and Damascus, provided my mother with the edge she needed in her barter relationship with Umm Samir. With so many red lipsticks coming all the way from Damascus, my mother over-stuffed her husband as well as her two little daughters until they could no longer stand one more lipstick delivery from Damascus.

Lacking the emotional resilience needed to visit my father's house in his hometown of Jaffa, the very first place I paid homage to when I came to Palestine in 1981 was my parents' house in Jerusalem.

"Ah! You must be Siham's daughter, Siham Jabri-al-Amiry? Oh, my God! You look so much like her!" Salma, one of the late Umm Samir's three daughters, screamed her greeting at me when I appeared at my parents' huge terrace thirty-three years after they had left it in 1948. I wanted to see the terrace on which both my sisters, Arwa and Anan, had spent their Jerusalem childhood. "Aaaaah, take the sheep away from me! Take that sheep away from me! Poor thing, poor sheep, he is so scared of me!" Shaking, my three-year-old sister Anan had screamed when my Baba brought her first "temporary" pet to this huge terrace and the big garden below it.

Looking at Salma's pale and worn face I realised the significance of the lipstick-for-food-programme initiated by my flamboyant Damascene mother for the benefit of the provincial looks and tired faces of Jerusalemite women.

Unable to sleep, I rolled onto my right side again.

I then reached for the transistor radio I had placed under my pillow. Soon I was lost in an ocean of Hebrew. Some stations

6

were coming through crystal clear, including Kol Israel and Kol Yerushalayim, while the Arabic stations were hissing. I could not but recall some of the stories that Baba had told us over the years about the very first Palestine Broadcasting Service[1], Huna al Quds (Jerusalem Calling). It was a British Mandate state-owned radio station where he worked in the early 1940s until it was taken over by the Zionist forces in 1948.

Baba told sad and funny stories whenever our family sat for dinner around that long dining table in our house in Amman. I smiled in bed as I remembered how his *strict* eating habits were similar to Umm Salim's, my late mother-in-law. Not only did Baba keep a rigid British Mandate schedule for the three meals: eight, two and eight, he also imposed conversation rules. In addition to him and Mama, each one of us four children had to tell a joke or summarise what she or he had learnt that day.

While Mama's stories focused on the glory of her Damascene family, particularly her rich and good-looking father, my Baba's often had a historical, political or nationalist twist to them. In spite of the many personal and national losses he suffered – lost homes, a lost city, a dispersed family, a lost and shattered homeland, as well as a broadcasting station – he, like most of his Nakba generation, shied away from talking about his personal pain and immersed himself in starting a new life, with a new job, a new house, and a new everything in Diaspora.

Perhaps the wound was still open.

It was much later in my life that I realised:

While the Palestinians try hard to forget when they should remember.

The Israelis try hard to remember when they should forget.

---

[1] "The Palestine Broadcasting Service was second in the region after Radio Cairo, and was established by the British Mandate authorities in order to have an influential media tool and influence the Arab masses towards British policies in the region." *Source:* Wikipedia.

While the Palestinians refuse to be victims, the Israelis make sure that they remain the only victims.

My childhood memories oscillated between Mama's omnipresent family mansion in the splendour of the old city of Damascus, and Baba's lost house in the Manshiyeh neighbourhood of the sea town of Jaffa. I had to construct this house from tales and imagine it from far, far away.

But I must say, in spite of his great losses and seriousness, Baba had a great sense of humour and appreciated a good story.

It was around that dining table that I had to figure out what a joke was. While my brother Ayman, two years older than me, told truly funny stories and hilarious jokes, I, the baby of the family, told the same joke every time we sat around the table, over and over again. And since every single member of my family began rolling with laughter the minute I opened my mouth I concluded that a joke gets better and funnier the more often it is told. Perhaps there is a clue here to my adult style of talking and writing.

Unable to sleep, I turned over in bed.

I surfed through more Hebrew wavelengths and thought again about Baba's lost station. From his hometown, Jaffa, he had gone to study biology at the American University of Beirut in 1924. Eager to serve his wounded country he returned home at the age of twenty-one. He helped establish a chapter of the Arab Students Club along with other nationalist activists, but soon took refuge in Jordan in order to avoid an arrest order issued by the British Mandate authorities in Palestine on the eve of the 1929 Buraq uprising.[2]

After spending more than ten years as the principal of the only high school in the Jordanian town of Salt, Baba was

---

[2] The 1929 uprising was an Arab revolt against British Mandate policies favouring the migration of European Jews to Palestine.

8

delighted to accept a position as the head of the Arabic Programme on the Palestine Broadcasting Service (PBS) in 1942, also known as the Palestine Broadcasting Corporation (PBC).

On March 30, 1936 the Palestine Broadcasting Service was inaugurated with programmes running in three languages, Arabic, Hebrew and English, and airtime allocated in that order. "Not having the letter *p* in Arabic, most Arabs pronounced it as *b*. So there was tremendous confusion between the PBC and the BBC. But this was not the first time the British had taken credit both for things they do, and things they do not do." I can still hear Baba's chuckles and see his sparkling dark eyes as he told the story around that dining table.

While Mama was busy raising her two little daughters and improving her barter programme with her Jerusalem neighbours, Baba was in constant negotiation with the British Mandate authorities in order to gain better terms and longer airtime for his Arabic programmes on the PBC/BBC.

With tension rising and fighting escalating between Arab and Jewish forces in Jerusalem, Mama felt the need to enroll in a first aid course. Realising that his biology degree got him nowhere in the increasingly lawless jungle called Palestine, Baba, like Mama, opted for further education and began working towards a law degree at the Arab College in Jerusalem.

Meanwhile, in view of their biased policies favouring the Zionists, the British officers kept all Arabic programmes under heavy scrutiny and tight censorship. This inevitably resulted in the resignation of many Palestinians working in the Arabic section. Among those who resigned were Dad's best friends: Ibrahim Tuqan, a famous Palestinian poet, and Khalil Sakakini, the eminent Palestinian educator who handed in his resignation to his British boss the minute he heard the Jewish broadcaster announce on air, "This is *Eretz Israel*."

"If this is *Eretz Israel*, then where is *Ard Falastin* (the land of Palestine)?" yelled Khalil Sakakini at his British superior.

"Well, he says his point of view and you say yours," explained the British officer.

"What point of view? Why does he call it *Eretz Israel* when the official name of this station is the Palestine Broadcasting Service?"

From what Baba reported, it seemed that both the Arabic as well as the Jewish programmes had become platforms for national awareness, debates and, of course, conflicts, and hence targets for sabotage.

On August 3, 1939, the Jewish underground militia, Etzel, blew up part of the radio station's offices during the children's hour. Two of its staff were killed in the sabotage bombing: a Palestinian called Adib Mansour, and a new Jewish immigrant from South Africa named Mae Weissenberg.

In spite of the danger of it all, Mama had been delighted to leave the little provincial town of Salt and come running to what turned out to be her favourite city: Jerusalem and its stuffing(s).

Sleeping on my back, the radio pressed against my left ear wailing Hebrew songs, and I could not but recall how happy Baba was when he told us a story about an Arab singer who had visited the station. Many came to perform in the live music programmes of the PBC, mostly Egyptians, but also Syrians and Lebanese. "I was so fortunate to meet them all in person: Abdulwahab, Zakaria Ahmad, Saleh Abdulghani, Lur Dukkash, and of course Asmahan and her brother, Farid al-Atrash." So different in appearance, I could never remember that the two renowned Lebanese singers, Asmahan and Farid al-Atrash (paradoxically, *atrash* in Arabic means deaf) were sister and brother. When Asmahan was killed in a car accident there were strong rumours that the 'accident' was orchestrated either by

British intelligence, as many believed she was their agent, or by Umm Kulthum, the Maria Callas of the Arab world and Asmahan's only real competitor.

One thing I remember vividly is how much Baba and Mama wished Umm Kulthum would return to Jerusalem and to the Arabic programmes of the PBC.

Umm Kulthum had actually visited Jerusalem and other cities in Palestine in 1935, only a year before the inauguration of the PBS. I, like the rest of my family, was a big fan of hers, so I had memorised all the dates of her performances in Palestine by heart. The poster which my mother had framed and placed on the wall of our living room had Umm Kulthum's photo as well as the following text with dates and cities:

In the flourishing cities of Palestine the great singer Umm Kulthum and her celebrated band present the following concerts:

May 1, 2 in Jerusalem (Cinema Edison)
May 5, 6 in Jaffa (Theatre Opera Maghribi)
May 7, 8 in Haifa (Cinema 'Ein Dour)

Indeed, much had happened in the course of the ten years that separated Umm Kulthum's performances in the 'flourishing cities of Palestine', and May 1948 when the British left Palestine and all hell broke loose.

They Missed Mama's Cooking

On May 4, 1948
Having fulfilled their promise
A Jewish state over Palestine
The British packed up and went home
They claimed they missed their mothers' cooking
Roast beef and Yorkshire pudding
With boiled cabbage on the side

11

They simply boarded their ships and sailed away
Without a word of apology
Or farewell
The Bride was never consulted
Not in 1918 when they first landed
Nor in 1924 when Lord Balfour made his declaration
What God did not do for centuries
Lord Balfour delivered in sixty-seven words
When they arrived her name was Palestine
And when they left her name had become Israel
Being impartial rulers
Some subjects were more equal than others
They handed the new minority the majority of the land
Equity and more equity in the Empire where the sun never
    sets

May 4 of 1948
They left behind two fighting peoples
One strengthened, the other weakened
The new and mighty jubilated and went for more
"What is mine is mine and what is yours is also mine"
Meanwhile the old and the frail, dispossessed and
    dehumanised
Were left to mourn and lament

They mourned the larger-than-life losses
They mourned the loss of a home, of a garden, an orchard, a
    field, a homeland.
The loss of a sea, of mountains, hills, plains, valleys, lakes, springs,
    riverbeds, archaeological sites, Bedouin hamlets, villages,
    towns and cities.
They mourned the loss of a sun dipping in an open
    Mediterranean Sea.
The workers mourned the loss of their factories; the
    professionals mourned the loss of their offices.

The merchants mourned the loss of their suqs and markets: the buzz and noise of the old town of Acre, of Haifa, Jaffa, Lod, Ramallah, Asqalan and of Asdoud.

They mourned mosques, churches, holy shrines and monasteries

The sick missed their doctors, clinics, pharmacies and hospitals, and a few missed their mental clinics. The fishermen mourned the loss of their sea: the uncertainty of venturing into the darkness of a treacherous sea; and their full nets at sunrise after yet another night of fishing; they missed their companions: other fishermen in small boats; they missed the big and small fish: sea bass, sardines, calamari, shrimp and the reddish Sultan Ibrahim (red mullet) that brought them luck, but also the rare sharks of the deep sea and those of the seashore.

The peasants mourned the loss of their compact villages and vast fertile fields: the orange groves, the vineyards, the ancient olive trees, the shade of a fig tree, the flowering almond trees, the burgundy splashes of the mulberry and pomegranate trees, the thistles of the cacti.

The kids missed school but also playing in the narrow alleys, dipping their feet in the salty sea and its fine sandy beaches, riding on small donkeys and hanging down deep water cisterns.

But most of all they mourned the loss of a *home*.

They simply missed *home*: they missed their fruit gardens, their living rooms, their bedrooms, their balconies, the dining rooms and tables, the formal guest room and the worn-out sofas, their Persian carpets, their books and their paintings, cups and crystal glasses, kitchen cupboards full of seasonal foods and extra virgin olive oil pressed that year, shelves heavy with wedding china, closets full of old and new clothes.

They mourned the loss of a musical instrument: an oud, a drum, a hand-held daf, and possibly a piano. They mourned leaving behind their photo albums and letters from a mother to

13

her child, they missed their children's toys, teenage 78 rpm records, personal book collections. They mourned their public libraries, schools, kindergartens, football fields, hospitals, clinics, stores, cars, tractors, buses, motorcycles, bicycles, toddlers' toy cars and swings.

And when they had time to reflect on the *animals* they had left behind, they cried: whatever happened to the cows, horses, sheep, goats, mules, camels, donkeys, ducks and chickens, rabbits, turtles, beloved dogs and cats, and lovebirds in cages?

And who watered the thirsty horses when their owners had to run for their lives?

Ah, if only animals told their stories
Before they died in silence.

As Diaspora ended for one people
Diaspora started for another
A new nation remembered, an old one forgotten.

Unable to sleep, I turned on my back and took a deep breath.

When the fighting between Arabs and Jews intensified in 1948, trying to spare his baby, Baba spent most of his days and nights at the PBS studios in the new broadcasting building in Talbiyeh, which later became a West Jerusalem neighbourhood.

Meanwhile Mama bore the heavy burden of protecting her four dear ones: her two daughters, Arwa and Anan, aged five and four, and their two little puppies, one-year-old sister and brother, Lulu and Murjan.

And once again, with the help of her rich uncle's Abdo Taxi Company, Mama managed a swift trip to her family in Damascus where she left Arwa and Anan. When she hurried back she arrived to a half-occupied house and two missing puppies.

Since our home, the Ghosheh house, was strategically located it was often caught in the crossfire. Four of the Zionist fighters

14

took refuge in our living room. Mama was assigned the task of negotiating with the occupiers, but as is often the case, what was fully and rightfully ours had already become half theirs; and like the rest of Jerusalem and Palestine, part of our house and Mama's *jhaz* (dowry) furniture fell under occupation.

As for the missing reddish-brown puppies (hence the name Murjan or coral), while Umm Samir claimed enemy fighters had stolen Lulu and Murjan, others swore that the cute little puppies had been brutally slain. Hoping it was theft rather than the unspeakable, Mama's eyes flooded with tears.

With the help of Ammu Adli, a family friend and a good neighbour, she loaded her share of her own dowry furniture into the back of a truck.

Off she went in the direction of Ramallah.

Like the black table around which we gathered years later, telling jokes and stories of hope and aspiration for a new and happy life in Amman, the rest of the furniture had either been grazed by bullets or pierced by direct hits: all witnesses to what Mama and Baba had been through.

"Mama, did you bring Lulu and Murjan with you?" This was the very first question that little Arwa and Anan asked as they ran to welcome their mother who eventually rejoined them in Damascus. It was this innocent inquiry, in the safety of her family home, that finally made Mama surrender. She burst into sobs as she knelt down and hugged her two little ones.

It took my sister Anan some forty years to dig into her past and write her first short story titled, "Lulu and Murjan."

Meanwhile, back in Jerusalem, Baba alongside his friend and colleague, Ajaj Nuwayhid, the head of cultural programmes at PBC, and many others, carried on with the heavy responsibility of moving the broadcasting equipment from Jerusalem to Ramallah where the main transmitter was.

For the following few months, the whole family, Baba, Mama,

Arwa and Anan worked, lived and played in the corridors of the transmission building, today's Muqata'a, the Presidential Headquarters: the very same building in which the late Arafat was besieged and heavily bombarded (along with my mother-in-law) in 2003.

Ah, if only buildings could tell their stories.

"If only your Baba loved me as much as he loved his radio station and equipment!" Mama kept complaining over the next decades.

Whether she was right or (more probably) wrong about my being conceived in the Holy City, Jerusalem, you have a piece of my heart.

Yes, you have a piece of my heart.

No, not because you have been so idolised and iconised.

No, not because you've been declared the "Eternal Capital" in a doomed world.

No, not because of your fabricated past that has been made more important than your present.

It is because you were not allowed to be a "normal" city with normal people, so much so that you have become an abnormal place with abnormal people – Arabs and Jews alike.

Jerusalem, you have a piece of my heart only because you have a chunk of my *mundane everyday life*.

Yes, you were the very first city to welcome me back when I arrived in Palestine in the summer of 1981. I vividly recall how I hurriedly dropped my suitcase and ran out of the YMCA where I was staying, soon to be lost in your crowded suqs and narrow, labyrinthine alleys. I, slowly but cautiously, had to build my relationship with you: a familiar, yet very peculiar, city. Mama was right: your people are certainly aloof and reserved.

It was in Jerusalem that my husband-to-be Salim and I had our first rendezvous: he took me to see Lady Chatterley's Lover (I mean the film).

Whenever I had a chance, Salim next to me, I would excitedly drive the fourteen kilometers separating the confining and provincial town of Ramallah, where we both lived (separately), from the big and open city.

I would park my little Fiat 127 in East Jerusalem to avoid having it towed away or blown up in West Jerusalem. The blue plates revealed that its owner was potential trouble. And since it was not so long ago that the Israeli Army had blown up Rema's UN car I made sure to take care of my little baby, my precious set of wheels.

We would then venture *west* for long strolls that took us everywhere and nowhere: to Jaffa Street, to Stiematsky's bookshop, to the Orthodox Mea She'arim Quarter for its charm and peculiarity, or to the German Colony neighbourhood for a good coffee and scrumptious German pastry, to the Talbiyeh neighbourhood to visit our dear friend, Judy Blanc, or to walk around admiring the architectural qualities of the Yemin Moshe. And since the Israelis had closed all the movie theatres in Ramallah and the other cities in the Occupied Territories, including East Jerusalem, and since Salim is a passionate movie-goer, we more often than not found ourselves in an Israeli cinema.

Seeking atonement for violating the boycott of enemy territory and products, we would eventually settle down to a nice meal, with terrible local wine, in one of Arab East Jerusalem's restaurants.

I must admit that the only time I did *not* feel guilty *not* boycotting Israeli products was when it came to wine. I tipsily convinced myself that the excellent Golan Heights wines made by Israelis were kosher because they came from the occupied parts of Syria. Compared to the local Palestinian wines produced by Cremesan and Latrun, two Italian monasteries, Israeli wines were far superior. Having been away from home too long to remember how good Italian wines taste, the Italian nuns and monks had acquired local Palestinian taste (or perhaps the lack of it). Thanks to the superb made-in-Ramallah arak, I was able to stick, more often than not, to my boycott of Israeli goods, one of the few principles I have left.

Tipsy, Salim and I would spend the rest of the evening on the lovely terrace of the National Hotel, the same hotel in which I was allegedly conceived in one of the rooms, not so many decades earlier. Meanwhile the owners, the Abu al-Haj family, were struggling to keep it afloat in the impossible economic conditions of East Jerusalem. Sadly, it has since closed down.

Beginning to fall asleep now, my other Jerusalem connections raced through my mind: Riwaq architectural projects, friends, Hakawati Theatre plays, Orient House and negotiating at 'Peace Talks,' applying for visas and attending boring receptions at consulates, shopping, and finally, having to use the passport belonging to my dog, the late Nura, just to enter the city.

And look at me now, sneaking in like a thief, committing a series of 'criminal offences' and 'illegally' crossing the many checkpoints that strangle you, Jerusalem.

I come to listen to your pain and to hear the stories and memories of a few of your obsessed citizens.

Jerusalem, I come to you in disguise: in over-colourful, immodest clothes and vulgar make-up ... The only way I could come to you was in disguise, as a whore.

Unable to sleep, I turned over and switched on the light.

Come on, Suad, take it easy on yourself.

It was three in the morning when I marvelled at the reflection of light on an intricately spun spider's web stretched between two elaborate cast-iron window guards. Something about the spider's energy and movements made me think of Ranjani, Mama's domestic helper, who was far from home and whose house – as well as twenty-four years' worth of work – was swept away by the 2004 tsunami that hit the southern coast of her native Sri Lanka. In spite of all that, Ranjani carried on.

18

I thought of Vanouch, my Armenian-Greek-Cypriot friend, (married to a Palestinian) whose home ended up on the other side of Nicosia, and who burst into tears when the young wife of the Turkish officer told her that the chimney in that house was a new addition. "It was *my father* who built this chimney *with his own hands.*"

I thought of Ritu, my Indian friend and publisher, who had lost a home in what became Pakistan.

I thought of Shams, my Pakistani friend, who misses her home in Delhi. I thought of our London-based friend, Sami Zubaida, an Iraqi Jew, who misses home: Baghdad and its Tigris.

And that made me think of the Jewish communities who not long ago were an integral part of the former Arab world.

I thought of the Native Americans and the Aborigines of Australia.

I must have dreamt of black Africans being dragged a long, long way from home.

Like most of us, never to *feel at home* again.

And as I was falling asleep, I wondered why other peoples' pain makes me feel better.

I heard the loud beat and humming of drums coming all the way from deepest Africa, only to wake up and realise that it was my friend Huda who had been banging hard on my bedroom door.

"Suad! Suad! Yalla, habibti, get up. Drink your coffee. I want you fully awake. I've made you lots of appointments today, including one with PM Golda Meir. I am going to show you the biggest real estate robbery in modern history."

Come on, Suad, drink lots and lots of coffee.

Part Two

Andoni: A Master Builder's Passion

Andoni

For years he stood in solitude across the street from the beloved.
And for hours on end he stared *west* waiting for the sun to rise.
Only death could have set them apart
And it did.

2

The Smile

Pash Muhandis Andoni Baramki, far right

There seem to have been no disasters, natural or otherwise, the year he was born.
It wasn't 1898, the year of the five harsh snowstorms
Nor was it 1915, the year of the locusts
Nor 1927, the year of the destructive earthquake
Not even a war or an uprising

The faded Arabic inscription on his gravestone in Ramallah's Christian Orthodox cemetery reads:

Andoni Jubra'il Ya'qub Baramki
Born in Jerusalem (January 1894)
Died in Ramallah (September 1972)
14 kms. away from the beloved

Next to Andoni's gravestone is his wife's:

Evelyn Khouri–Baramki
Born in Jaffa (April 1906)
Died in Ramallah (June 2004)
44 kms. away from her beloved hometown, Jaffa

Twelve years seemed to be the appropriate age difference between the well-established architect-groom and his bride.
His year of birth was calculated from her birth certificate.

This made sense to him.
It made sense to her.
And to everyone around them
Birth year established: 1894.

Name

His ageing half-Greek mother, Khariklia (not sounding too nice in Arabic, hence Farha) or Umm Ya'qub, who lived with him and his family, or more accurately, the other way round: they lived with her, called him Andoni with an accentuated *d*. Evelyn, his good-natured and humorous wife, sometimes called him Ton*i*, with a long *iii* for intimacy (*dala'*).

His Greek friends and classmates at the Academy of Fine Arts in Athens, including one who became the Benedictus (the Greek Orthodox Patriarch) of Jerusalem, called him Andonaiki.

An*d*oni, Ton*i* or Andonaiki were all names for the same saint: Mar Anton, a.k.a. St. Anthony, who is celebrated in January every year by all Jerusalem Christians, as well as Christians elsewhere in Palestine and Greater Syria. He, like all other Andonis, considered his name-day as his own birthday. Hence the day on which our Andoni was biologically born remains unknown. Birth month established: January 1894.

That smile

Andoni had a subtle smile: elusive, mysterious, restrained, abstract, ambiguous and indefinable. That smile was the most prominent feature of his well-defined face: a big round head, a big round nose, big protruding blue eyes and fleshy lips. It was difficult to figure out or explain what that enigmatic smile was about.

Khariklia, his mother, thought the innocent smile reflected a kind heart.

Evelyn, his wife, thought the adorable smile reflected a joyful husband.

His friends thought the peaceful smile reflected *saber* Ayyoub (the patience of Job), a tolerant and sincere friend.

But no one, not even his mother, could recall whether Andoni was born with that smile or whether he had slowly acquired it to reflect a life of varied experiences. Unlike the year and month in which he was born, the date that peculiar smile appeared was never established.

Work

It took the powerful and devastating earthquake of 1927 for people to realise the similarity between Andoni and his buildings: both were well-built and structurally sound. While numerous buildings in Jerusalem and other cities were badly damaged, *all* of Andoni's buildings stood proud.

So did he.

That catastrophic earthquake generated numerous architectural projects for the master architect, Andoni Baramki, his Jewish draftsman, Abraham Cherniak and foreman, Ginsburg, a German immigrant who changed his name to Ben Hurin in 1949.

From the year of the earthquake and from his Jerusalem office, Andoni's secular and religious projects spread all over Palestine, in cities and villages alike, till his death in 1972.

Though a well-known Christian Orthodox, Andonaiki's earthquake reputation convinced various churches, including the Latin Patriarchate in Jerusalem, to transcend sectarianism and seek his help and protection – in addition to that of the Virgin Mary, of course.

For the Latin Patriarchate in Jerusalem, architect Andoni built St. Joseph School in the Old City, the beautiful Romanian Church and convent near the Jewish neighbourhood of Mea She'arim, and little chapels at the Baptism Site (al Maghtas) on the banks of the Jordan River. He also designed buildings in Ramallah, the small and lovely summer resort where in 1927 he had met his beloved Evelyn. There he built the Sam'an Daoud House, the Kassis house, today's Hotel Casa Nova (its original design was totally mutilated by the 1980 additions), and the Aruri house, also known as the Mukhtar's house, in the village of Burham.

While the world was suffering from an economic depression in the late Twenties and Thirties of the twentieth century,

Jerusalem was witnessing a construction boom. Whole neighbourhoods, mansions, villas and apartment buildings were mushrooming on the hilly landscape around the Old City. Andoni's villas were the icing on the cake. His buildings sprang up in the new residential neighbourhoods: the Greek and German colonies, Musrara, Sa'ed o Said, Katamon, Talbiyeh and Upper and Lower Baq'a. A drive along the Jerusalem-Bethlehem road created the impression that Andoni was the only architect in town. "Baramki style" became the term to describe buildings distinguished by the use of the Jerusalem pink stone, *slayyeb,* highlighted with the addition of white stone for the round and pointed arches he often used.

The boom suggested that people built one villa to live in, another to rent out – or if economic means allowed, a complete apartment building. This was exactly what architect Andoni did for himself and his family in 1929 and 1932: he built one splendid villa in the Sa'ed o Said area and another across the road in the posh neighbourhood of Musrara – a masterpiece that he always referred to as "nour hayati" (the light of my life). "You are the light of my life."

But, as we all know, happiness and the good life never last long in the Holy Land, so as fighting between Arabs and Jews intensified in the spring of 1948, the Baramki family like thousands of other Palestinians, was forced to abandon their beautiful home and prosperous neighbourhood.

An orange cake and a knife to cut it with was all that Evelyn grabbed as the family frantically rushed out of the door. Everything happened in a panic following a bullet that grazed Evelyn's light brown hair. "*That is it*!" said Andoni as he broke a promise that he had made to himself – *never* to leave his home. But escape was their only choice as bullets rained through the shattering glass.

A hot orange cake in a hot baking tin

A knife

House keys

These became mementoes of a distant past.

Andoni, Evelyn, Laura, sixteen, and George, thirteen, raced out of that house. They would never be allowed into it again.

To his misfortune, the light of his life ended up on the border of what had become Jewish West Jerusalem, less than a kilometer away from what became Arab East Jerusalem. The Israeli army on the western side, and the Jordanian army on the eastern side, like the two villas, faced one another.

The Baramki villas, Andoni's,

So close to his heart and eyes

So unreachable.

Longing

Jerusalem 1948–1967.

It was a crisp Saturday and the sun was setting

Like most other Saturdays, it was time for him to venture forth

He was apprehensive today, as he had been last Saturday

As he will be the following Saturday

From one war to another

He has been at it for nineteen years

From the '48 War till the '67 War

With a tiny difference:

With each new Saturday melancholy and grief intensified

Until death forced them apart

He looked left

He looked right

Then ducked his head

Bent his two-meter tall robust body

And swiftly sneaked into the stairway

None of his friends or the YMCA staff saw him vanish
Or so he thought
Or so they pretended
In spite of everything he still took the risk
To be the talk of the town
Or be caught or even shot at
And all that came with it:
The embarrassment of his three kids
The jealousy of his beautiful wife
And the reprimand of his mother

Love was stronger
A love that turned into a lifelong *obsession*
With the lightness of an Arab horse he elegantly trotted up
    the stairs
And in no time he was at the top of the four-storey stairway
And in no time he was face to face with the barrier he hated
    most:
The heavy and rusty iron gate that never failed to reveal to
    the enemy as well as the beloved the arrival of the crazed,
    the possessed.

He leaned his robust hot body against the cold surface of the
metal door, pushing at its rusty latch with his two oversized
sturdy palms. He stood perfectly still until autumn clouds
absorbed the amplified clank of the latch and the deafening
squeak of the rusted hinges. Then and only then did he venture
out onto the open roof of the building.

Every Shabat, at sunset, the roof of the YMCA, like all adjacent
roofs, was completely deserted. This he knew from past
experience. But for extra caution, once in the open, he ducked
his head and, stooping, almost crawled towards the western side
of the roof.

Like a child he crouched behind the white stone parapet and

stiffly stretched his long legs on the dirty roof. He rested his big head against the parapet and then, only then, took a deep breath. Andoni did his breathing exercises three times a week: once on the roof of this building and twice as the basso profundo of the Jerusalem Orthodox Choir. As much as he would have loved to sing for her on the occasion of their Saturday encounters, he kept his desire under control.

Having regained his energy and steadied his heartbeat, Andoni was ready for his weekly encounter.

He knelt down, straightened his shoulders, lifted his head above the parapet, and carefully looked over it. The second he saw her, tears formed and shone in his big blue eyes.

How much he missed her, how much he loved her.
How much he treasured her white and pink complexion
The soft light reflecting on an even softer, undulating body
He admired everything about her
Her shape
Her form
Her movements
Her flawlessly perfect proportions
The delightful floral ornaments
Everything about her was perfect
Every time he saw her or got close to her he surrendered his
    soul to the creator
Oh God, how beautiful she is
Tears ran down his cheek as he waved goodbye
She looked back at him, moaning softly
Then she smiled
He smiled back and walked away
Until next Saturday
Until the 1967 War
When he and his beloved were united once but *not* for all

Wars separate, others unite (perhaps: some wars separate, others unite)

Ramallah, Tuesday, June 6, second day of the 1967 War

The piercing shrieks of the F16 fighter jets over the skies of Ramallah made Andoni and Evelyn think the planes had just rocketed through their bedroom. Their daughter Laura, son Gabi, and his wife Haifa felt the same. They all ran out of their respective bedrooms to the semi-protected corridor.

Andoni's five grandchildren, Naila, Nadim, Hala, Hania and Maha expressed their fright by either wetting themselves or crying for hours on end. "Baba ... Baba ... *biddi* Bab*aaaa*", cried three-year-old Maha in search of her father, Doctor Abdallah, who had been stationed at a Bethlehem hospital ever since the war erupted. That was why Laura and her kids had taken refuge in her parents' house in Ramallah, away from Jerusalem where their home was. On the other hand, in Haifa's womb, no one could tell how foetus Hani reacted to the F16s. Haifa could not distinguish between her fearful heartbeats and her baby's fierce kicks.

The Baramkis, like everyone else, hoped that the hostilities which had begun early in the morning of the day before, would move west in the direction of Israel. But the F16s left them in no doubt that sleeping in their bedrooms on the ground floor was not safe. Shortly after, mattresses were laid on the cement floor of the unfinished basement of the house Andoni had built five years earlier, in 1962.

While everyone, including the smiling seventy-three-year-old Andoni, was busy moving furniture, helping to modify the living and sleeping arrangements for wartime, sweet and unruffled Evelyn carried on with her stress-free daily routine. Business as usual. Together with four of her grandchildren, Naila ten, Nadim eight, Hala six, and Maha three, she went for a short

31

walk in the surrounding terraced olive groves, followed by a coffee break with one of the neighbours.

Had Ramallah not been under curfew, and had the bus passed by that morning, she would have taken her grandchildren to visit Aunt Linda, a sister of hers, who lived in the neighbouring town of Birzeit.

To divert the shell-shocked grandchildren and give Laura a break from her kids Evelyn took them for a longer walk than usual. Once out of their mother's sphere of jurisdiction, Evelyn let go of the children's hands. She set them and herself free. While they frolicked in the empty streets of Ramallah, Grandma Evelyn sang at the top of her voice. Like everyone else in her family she had a beautiful and sensuous voice. It took the little children some time to realise that the high-pitched sounds that filled the skies above them did not originate from their Grandma's soprano but from the Israeli fighter planes.

Suddenly, the heavy-set Grandma and the little ones were running in terror as the F16 jets bombed targets close-by. They ran and ran; they ran and screamed; they screamed and tumbled to the ground, until the children were met by their hysterical mother.

Once Laura was wrapped protectively over her four kids, joining the cacophony of the Israeli fighter planes, her reprimanding screams started and would not end. When they rejoined the rest of the family in the congested basement, Evelyn became the bombing target in a family war that started then, but never ended:

Some screamed forever
Some cried forever
Some got depressed forever
Some, like Andoni, had a laughing fit
Which turned into an eternal cynical smile.

Even when Israeli soldiers came the next day, banging at his door and demanding the keys to Gabi's brand new Peugeot, Andoni continued to smile as he handed the keys over. Off the soldiers went on a sinister two-day mission. When they brought back the wreck of a car, Andoni walked around examining it. He took the keys and flashed his smile at them in return.

June 10, 1967

Curfews were prolonged.

War nights were also prolonged.

Not only for the smiling old man, but also for the baby in Haifa's womb.

In spite of all the havoc around him, or perhaps because of it, little Hani was curious and hence determined to make it into the noisy world around him. He kicked and jerked until his mother, Haifa and his father, Gabi drove their bashed-up car under fire to the French Hospital in East Jerusalem. That same day, Friday, June 10, little Hani was pulled out of his mother's womb and into a world of continuous action.

Despite yet another defeat – resulting in the occupation of the rest of Palestine: East Jerusalem, the West Bank and the Gaza Strip, as well as Syria's Golan Heights and Egypt's Sinai desert, and leading to the displacement of more Palestinians – Andoni's striking smile grew more pronounced by the day.

None of his family asked, nor did he explain.

"Come on kids, gather your things, we're going back home to Jerusalem!" Dr. Abdallah assertively announced as he hugged his wife Laura. She cried. No one could figure out why she cried, maybe it was happiness or exhaustion, perhaps both.

While the little children excitedly gathered their scattered toys and clothes, Grandpa Andoni rushed to his study.

Making sure to close the door behind him, Andoni opened and closed all the drawers in his room as quickly as possible. He then went through the neatly organised folders, the many old photo albums, some documents, and finally unrolled and rolled back some architectural drawings.

In no time he was standing by the front door, neatly dressed and ready to go. The size of the red file he hugged close to his chest, as well as the luggage next to him, gave the impression that he was leaving and never coming back. And when his sweetheart Evelyn asked: "Toniii, habibi, where are you going?" he replied with an unwavering smile: "I am going to visit the beloved."

"The beloved?" she exclaimed, then added: "Ah, you mean Hani, our new grandchild!"

Hesitantly he responded, "Oh yes, Hani, our beloved new-born grandchild." Relieved, she helped him out. He had totally forgotten about the family anxiety and that fearful and spooky drive that Gabi and Haifa had taken in their battered car under curfew.

"But where, how will you see him?" It occurred to her to ask.

"I am going to Jerusalem with Abdallah."

"Toniii! You are not serious, I hope! Abdallah came to take Laura and his kids home, he did not come to take you for a *mishwar,* a picnic. His car is full, but more importantly, I need you to be here with me and our grandchild, Hania."

Toni only stood there, smiling.

"And why this big smile?" It was the very first time anyone had commented on Andoni's enigmatic smile. Getting no response, Evelyn continued: "And you know well enough that Gabi and Haifa will not be back with little Hani for another week or so."

Her words fell on deaf ears.

Like a little child, Andoni ran to take the front seat, then stuck his head and part of his ample trunk out of the window. "I need to see everything," he announced.

"See what? All the destruction in Jerusalem?" Dr. Abdallah asked as he loaded the trunk with all the family luggage.

"Was there much destruction around the YMCA building?" Andoni asked, holding the red file tightly against his chest.

Laura smiled while her husband replied, "Andoni, I'm not sure. I, like you, have been stuck under curfew, but from the news I gathered that the fighting was mostly concentrated around the seam-line: Jabal al-Mukabber and the Mandelbaum Gate next to the YMCA area."

"Around the YMCA!" Andoni repeated, then pressed his big palm to his forehead.

The destruction around the YMCA area caused the adults to fall into a long silence which lasted the whole trip from Ramallah to Jerusalem.

"Off I go," declared Andoni as soon as they reached, slamming the car door behind him. He hugged his four grandchildren first, then his daughter Laura, and then Abdallah.

"Good bye, Jiddo," Nadim and his sisters called out.

"Take care, Baba, please don't do anything silly like Mama!" Laura said, referring to Evelyn's hazardous walk with the kids. Then Laura and Abdallah dashed into their deserted house with the kids in tow.

"Forgot your suitcase!" Abdallah yelled after Andoni.

"Will come back for it," he replied, looking back and waving his hand as his legs picked up speed.

Laura had already figured out that once that smile appeared on her Baba's face it meant that he was already lost in his own world. In a trance he walked into the city and, in the same state, talked his way past civilians and soldiers alike to the western side of the seam-line.

He was so determined that no one dared to challenge his urgent need to get some place and meet someone he had neither seen nor touched in almost two decades (1948-1967). Separation made it feel more like two centuries.

Love, war and trauma create a peculiar sense of time.

Andoni's pounding eager steps, the pumping of his accelerated heartbeat, the jingling of the keys as well as the sporadic shooting around him composed the background music, a symphony, to the lovers' encounter. The closer he got to her, the more dramatically the symphony echoed in his ears until there was a sudden silence.

Everything froze once he was face to face with the beloved.

He smiled, she smiled back at him.

He stretched out his hands and touched her soft texture and her undulating curves.

And when it was time to totally embrace her and enter, a man with a gun appeared from behind, and in a not-so-friendly fashion challenged, yelled and threatened, cursed and turned violent, finally brandishing his rifle and threatening to kill Andoni.

And that pulled the lovers apart once again.

In the years that followed, a solitary Andoni stood at a safe distance and stared at *the beloved*: the light of his life.

One small detail

Courtroom, October 1968

That morning Andoni woke up early, even though he hadn't slept at night. He was already clean-shaven and elegantly dressed. The dark navy-blue suit he had carefully picked for the occasion made him look like a shrewd businessman, rather than the casual yet tasteful architect that he was. The fat red file held close to his heart reflected the same degree of attention to detail.

Being positive and optimistic were two of Andoni's virtues, in addition to being patient – very patient, extremely patient. Patience was a distinctive quality of this branch of the Baramki family.

Many had been skeptical, some decidedly so, about Andoni's appeal to the enemy's courts in West Jerusalem. But love knows no boundaries, nor do Israeli courts. There was Andoni's two-meter tall body jumping up and down with joy, now that the Israeli court had indeed issued an eviction order against the Jewish squatter who had occupied his house: his rival with the gun.

Everything now seemed possible, so Andoni spent most of the family savings to hire the renowned Israeli lawyer, Avraham Ronen, for yet another case.

Not only had attorney Ronen won an eviction case, he had lately also won a case in which the Palestinian Tazzeez family were allowed back to live in their house on the eastern side of the seam-line, the 1949 Armistice Line. The Tazzeez house in Sa'ed o Said neighbourhood was once Andoni's own house; he had been forced to sell it when in 1945 his business went bankrupt. Despite this reminder of a sad chapter in his life, he was in seventh heaven about a rare case in which an Arab family had won the right to move back to their own house.

Andoni stood tall next to his assertive lawyer in the Israeli courtroom. As agreed, Mr. Ronen read a few introductory notes to remind the judge that this was only "a follow-up" on an already won case.

"Your Honour, thanks to the judgement of this court, now that the occupier of Architect Andoni's house has been evicted, my client Andoni is seeking a court ruling that would allow him to go home." Mr. Ronen smiled at Andoni and added, "Mr. Baramki, I hope you do not mind me calling you by your first name?"

Surprised by this unnecessary interruption, Andoni smiled back nervously at his lawyer who then carried on. "Well, Your Honour, we are seeking your respected court's permission to allow Mr. Baramki and his family to go back and live in their home in the Musrara neighbourhood."

Andoni was thrilled to hear the words, "Mr. Baramki and his family to go back and live in their home." His eyes sparkled. He also liked the use of the word "occupier" with reference to the Israeli squatter. If he succeeded in getting this small occupier out of his house perhaps he could eventually get the big Occupier out of his country. One thing at a time, he thought to himself.

"Well, Your Honour, in the fifty years of my long professional life, and of *all* that I have designed and built – houses, villas, apartment buildings, churches, hotels, office buildings – *this* happens to be my favourite. In all modesty, it is a masterpiece. I love it as much as I love my children and grandchildren, perhaps even more; you know what I call it? 'Nour hayati', and you know, Your Honour, what nour hayati means in Arabic? This villa in particular was ..."

The judge interrupted, "Of course I understand *Aghabic* and what *nough hayati* means, but Architect Baramki you can't possibly love a house or a villa more than you love your children. No, Pash Muhandis (honourable architect), that is neither possible nor appropriate." The judge affirmed his moral position on the issue.

To gain the judge's sympathy Andoni opted to justify his love, his obsession, by stepping forward and handing the judge a huge photo album of his splendid villa. The dated photos covering the span of years from 1948 to 1967 were all taken from a bird's eye view.

"Indeed, it is a gorgeous villa. You Aghabs know how to build beautiful houses. I myself live in an Aghab house," said the judge, smiling approvingly.

Andoni smiled back, while thinking to himself:

Not only did you take the whole of Palestine and all Palestinian property: our towns, villages, farms, orange groves, children's schools and playgrounds, hospitals, offices and banks; our markets, shops, big and small, buses, cars, seashores and boats; our cattle, sheep, camels, dogs, cats, chickens, donkeys, and our beautiful Arab horses; my architectural practice, my beautiful villa, my lush green gardens, my furniture, my piano, my Persian carpets, my books, my children's beds and toys, my mother's crochet box and novels and my wife's paintings and music books; our kitchen appliances and utensils: fridge, oven, water kettle, cutlery, cups, plates; and all my family photo albums – and yet you still have the effrontery to brag about it, "I myself live in an Aghab house!" Shameless!

Of course, a respected judge like yourself, like many other high-ranking government officials, army generals and senior officers, in return for kicking us out, you were all offered Arab houses in Arab neighbourhoods. Even your Golda Meir lived in an Arab house. Ask me, Judge, and I will tell you in whose house your respected Prime Minister lived. She also bragged about living in Harun al-Rashid's villa in the German Colony. Ask me and I will tell you that her villa belonged to our friends, the Bisharat family. Ask me, Judge, I know them, each and every one. Would Your Honour like a list of those of you who live in Arab houses that I built? And whose house is it that you live in and brag about, Your Honour? And you have the guts to tell us, "Ah, you must be Mr. Dajani! Ah, you must be Mr. Sakakini! Ah, you must be Mr. Nammari! Ah, you must be Mr. Baramki – because the water and electricity bills are still in your name." Why don't you send us the phone bills, too, so that we pay them for you, Your Honour?

Andoni contained the anger mounting inside him. Like most Palestinians he was more concerned with his personal gains: he was simply seeking a court ruling that allowed him to live in his house.

"Is there anything else you want to say or present, Architect Baramki?" inquired the judge as he continued flipping through the photos of the beautiful Arab villa.

"Yes, Your Honour. Here is the land deed and here is the

house *tabu* which was issued in 1932 when I completed work on the villa." Andoni carefully handed the judge the well-preserved legal documentation certifying his ownership of the land and the villa built on it. To Andoni's utter surprise the judge showed extreme interest in the *tabu*. This made Andoni feel that substantiating his ownership had finally paid off.

"And where did you obtain this deed, Mr. Baramki?" asked the judge.

"From the Jordanian Land Registry Office in Jerusalem." Andoni was growing truly hopeful that he might be able to set the record straight, both for his own house and for Palestine as a whole. The more the judge examined the land deed, as he had done with the photo album, the louder Andoni's heart throbbed.

"Architect Baramki, you seem to be a rich man, but of course most architects are, they make a draft of your house and then a draft on your bank account! Hahaha!!" The judge laughed so much it seemed it was the first time he had heard his own joke.

"Isn't it better than drafting your children into so many wars, Your Honour? How many of them so far?" It was not clear whether the *how many* referred to the number of wars or the number of children drafted. Now it was Andoni's turn to laugh at his own joke. Since Arabs and Israelis do not laugh at each other's jokes, each had to tell and laugh at his own.

"Mr. Baramki, we are not here to talk politics. Let us stick to your case."

"Then here are the blueprints for my house." Andoni presented a large set of drawings that covered the judge's high podium.

A long pause followed, with neither one seeming to know where to go next. Then the judge spoke, looking Andoni straight in the eye: "Well, Mr. Baramki, the matter is obviously *not that simple.*"

"*Not that simple!* What is *not that simple?*" asked Andoni, taken aback.

"I mean to say," the judge now addressed the lawyer, "that I am sure both you and your client, Architect Baramki, realise that it is not a simple matter, Mr. Baramki moving back into his house in Musrara."

"Here are the house keys," said Andoni, pulling out the bunch of keys he had carried in his pocket for the last twenty years. This brought a glimmer to his eyes, but he quickly reined in his emotions and continued. "One week to whitewash and paint the house, another few days to clean it up, then a few truckloads of furniture and my family and I would be settled back in our home. How much simpler could it be? It only needs your consent, Sir."

"Well, Mr. Baramki, I wish it were that simple, but unfortunately it is not. It is not that simple," he repeated, trying to placate Andoni. "It is true that you have won the case for evicting the Jewish squatter from your house, but that does not *automatically* mean you can move there to live in it, just like that."

Andoni only found hope in the judge saying "your house," which was in itself an acknowledgement, and in his use of the word "automatically," which could imply that while it was not automatic, it could still happen.

"Mr. Baramki, I must compliment you on all the interesting documents, photos and drawings that you have kept of your house for all these years, and now the house keys, but I am afraid there is an important small *detail* that you seem to have missed… You are an *absentee*," the judge declared after a pause.

"Absentee?" Andoni looked questioningly at his lawyer, who remained silent.

"Yes, as far as the law is concerned, you are an *absentee*. You are an absentee landlord and consequently your house is *absentee property*." Realising the absurdity of what he had just said the judge avoided looking at Andoni.

"Absent? Absent?? How can I be absent?" Andoni kept repeating until he was interrupted.

"An *absentee*," the judge corrected him.

"An absentee, how can I be an absentee when I am standing right in front of Your Honour?"

"Well, as I am sure Mr. Ronen knows very well, as far as Israeli law is concerned you are an absentee landlord," the judge coldly reiterated, addressing the Israeli lawyer over Andoni's protestations.

"But, Sir, in this case, in *my* case, as you can very well see, neither I nor the house from which you evicted the squatter are absent."

"Mr. Baramki, I understand your frustration, but as I explained to you and to your lawyer, Mr. Ronen, *as far as Israeli law is concerned* you are an absentee landlord, and hence your house is absentee property. There is nothing I can do about this fact."

"Fact! I am an absentee landlord and my property is also absentee?" Andoni repeated in disbelief.

Sensing Andoni's anger the judge added, "It's nothing personal, Mr. Baramki; there are hundreds of thousands of Arabs who are considered absentees, just like you. All Palestinian refugees, whether present or absent, are considered absentees," explained the judge.

"Sir, the Palestinians are 'absentees' *only* because you do not allow them to be present. And those of us who are present are considered absent. We can never win."

"True, some of you are physically here."

"That 'some of you' numbers hundreds of thousands, Sir."

"Yes, I know. With all due respect, it's nothing personal, Pash Muhandis."

Andoni opened and closed his two large fists, stretched ten long fingers, and then started beating them against his body, as if reassuring himself that it was *present* and accounted for. He

42

began pounding his chest, picking up speed and force, then moved downwards to his stomach, abdomen, and upper thighs, all the while chanting, to the triple beat of his drumming fingers: "*Ab*-sen-tee, *ab*-sen-tee, *ab*-sen-tee!"

"Well, in this case you are both present and absent at the same time. You belong to the '*present absentee*'[3] category," said the judge.

"Is this a philosophical, existential matter, Sir?" Andoni asked incredulously, glancing at his lawyer.

The judge was clearly losing interest in the existential crisis he had provoked in Andoni, or for that matter in his *essential existence* altogether. Meanwhile, Andoni's smile was widening. It seemed to pull the judge back in so he said, "No, Mr. Baramki, this is not philosophical, it is the law, Israeli law."

Andoni thought it best to let go of all existentialist arguments – at least for the time being – opting instead for a commonly used line of argument that all Palestinians, and Israelis for that matter, use to win any debate: "Sir, I am from Jerusalem; I was born in Jerusalem, as were my father and my grandfather and my great-great-grandfather. I was raised in Jerusalem; I live in Jerusalem; I worked in Jerusalem; I got married in Jerusalem; I raised my family in Jerusalem and built many buildings and houses in Jerusalem, in Jerusalem … in Jerusalem …"

Having heard this argument so many times the bored judge began to yawn.

Realising that historical facts do not resonate with Israeli judges, Andoni shifted to logic and common sense: "Your Honour, why is it that when it comes to paying taxes to the Israeli government you do not consider us absentees, but when it comes to getting our property back then we are considered

---

[3] Present Absentee is an Israeli legal status that applies to all the Palestinians who stayed on their lands after the wars of 1948 and 1967. They and their properties are considered absent.

absentees? No one ever told me you are an absentee hence you should not pay the *arnona* (Israeli property tax)."

The judge had almost dozed off. Catching himself about to snore, he shook his head, straightened his posture and addressed Baramki in a tone that indicated he wished to conclude the matter. "Well, Mr. Baramki, I am afraid that is the *law.*"

"Which law? What law, Sir?" Andoni was growing desperate.

"What law? Israeli law, of course."

"If Israeli law rules that I am an absentee when I am standing right in front of Your Honour, then what does *Your Honour* say about that?"

"I, of course, follow the law," replied the judge.

"And who made this law, Sir?" asked Andoni.

"The government."

"Sir, do you see a human being in front of you? Or do you only hear the voice of a ghost?"

"Do you think I am blind?" the judge fired back. "Case dismissed."

He rose abruptly, walked out of the room and shut the door behind him.

The Israeli lawyer escorted absentee Andoni out of the courtroom.

Andoni stood in the court lobby staring at all those around him gathered there to seek Israeli justice.

Soon his smile turned into giggles
His giggles into chuckles
He could no longer hold back his laughter
He first rolled with laughter
Then bent over
Holding his stomach, then his abdomen
Soon he rolled on the floor, on his back, feet up and kicking
   in the air

Laughter filled the air
There was laughter, more laughter, and still more laughter
Until the laughter subsided
Then there was silence
More silence until
Silence prevailed
Stillness prevailed
Dead silence prevailed

3
Museum of Tolerance and Co-existence

The Baramki House

Those who have children never die. (*Illi khallaf ma mat*)

– Arabic proverb

Gabi: Andoni's eldest son

June 12, 1983 was a Sunday

He, like everyone else, stood in line.
The queue was long. Like his father, he was patient
So he waited.
Soon he found himself in the midst of a turbulent ocean:
An animated, loud crowd of young men and women
A bit irritated
Still he waited
What was I like at their age? he asked himself:
A moment for contemplation

At their age, at eighteen

In October 1946, almost eighteen, he, like them, was very keen to learn about the world. He wanted to go beyond the boundaries of a protective family and a wounded country. Beirut, the jewel of the Arab world with its American University, was his goal.

In April 1948, during his second year at the University, Gabi found himself cut off from both family and homeland. He waited many restless days, long sad months and an endless year to re-unite with his family. It was summer '49 in the city of Gaza.

"An orange cake, but no *family albums!*" protested Gabi, tears filling his big brown eyes as he suddenly realised that he had lost his past, his childhood and teenage memories. There was no proof that he had ever had a life in Jerusalem; there was no way home.

A photo album meant existence.

But all he could do at that moment was to vow not to eat orange cake ever again.

At their age, almost eighteen

At their age I was on the shores of Lebanon, he thought to himself again. No, he was not swimming or sunbathing, as first fantasised. Together with his teenage friends, he had lent a hand in pitching tents and setting up refugee camps.

The exodus from Palestine to Lebanon brought thousands of refugees. Like waves they arrived, and like waves their spirits and aspirations crashed against the reality of their new lives as their crowded boats ground ashore.

Gabi found himself face to face with his uncle, Wadi Khouri. With him – Gabi could hardly believe his eyes – were Aunt Salma and their children, Toni, Eliana and Zahi. Their other daughter Fifi, with her husband and two-year-old daughter were also there. They had fled the heavily bombarded city of Jaffa.

As more and more refugees stepped off the boats on the shores of the Mediterranean, more were arriving on foot. Yes, on foot. But whichever way they arrived, none had an inkling of what to do next, or where to go!

At their age, at eighteen, Gabi, like the rowdy youths around him, must have been strong: thirty-five years later the temporary wooden posts that he and his sturdy friends had planted deep in Lebanese soil had turned into permanent concrete poles.

As permanent as the refugees' sense of estrangement, and as deep as their sense of loss, which remained with them wherever they spread:

To the shores of Lebanon
To Syria's many oases
To the flooded river banks of Cairo and Baghdad
To Jordan's plains and deserts
To the hot sand dunes of Kuwait, Saudi Arabia and the Arab Gulf
To Tunis and Libya, to this Arab capital or that
To sub-Saharan Africa

To Paris, to New York
To Havana, Rio de Janeiro, Santiago
They dispersed
In exile

And now Gabi, at fifty-three, was patiently waiting in line for the grand opening of a new museum in Jerusalem. No more reflections on an unfortunate and sad past. "Live the moment," he instructed himself.

While everyone around him, young and old, locals and tourists, chatted and giggled, his silence deepened; a knot formed in his chest. With every slow step closer to the Museum, Gabi's anxiety increased. "What is it?" he asked himself.

Everything about the crowd around him made him sad, very sad.

Their laid-back attitude
Their joyfulness
The little anecdotes and quips
The mundane topics of their chatter
Their indifference to it all
Especially to his pain
The simple things in life that they took for granted
The normality of their lives

That's what got to him most: they were acting like *normal* people in a *normal* country

And this reminded him of his and his people's great losses.

Only then did he realise what he missed the most: a mundane life. He missed having a normal life.

Yes, it was *normality* that he missed most.

"For God's sake, stop it," Gabi yelled at the two teenage boys who interrupted his daydream, or rather nightmare. They were shoving one another. He turned back and stared at them. He then checked the queue.

It was still long.

So he waited.

Realising that neither justice nor normality were around the corner, Gabi decided to unwind. He pulled the new museum's brochure out of a file. The design was rather weak and unattractive, he thought. Let alone its content:

THE TOURJEMAN POST

For a better understanding of
Jerusalem's recent history
Overlooking the former mandelbaum gate
area, the Tourjeman post was a frontier
position during the period when Jerusalem
was divided (1948-1967) it has now been
restored and is dedicated to the theme:
Jerusalem – a divided city reunited

permanent exhibition
observation terrace
audio-visual programme
video films
reference library
open: Sunday – Thursday, 9 am – 4 pm
        Friday 9 am – 1 pm
Chail Handassa st. 4 tel. 281278
buses 1, 11, 27, 99

To him it was obvious that the light blue colour of the brochure recalled the Israeli flag, but still they could have chosen a more interesting shade of blue. He wasn't impressed by the quality of paper either. But worst of all were the layout and the many typos. The latter truly got to him. As president of Birzeit University, Dr. Gabi Baramki always read and re-read every single university publication. He made sure not to allow any typo to escape his scrutiny.

Gabi carried on with his impossible editorial mission: M*andelbaum* and G*ate* should start with capital letters: "Overlooking the *former* mandelbaum gate," it read. He gazed at the word "former" and wondered how many of the Israeli youngsters realised that the queue in which they were standing right now delineated the divide between East and West Jerusalem. The "Green Line", which far from being green, is rather dusty, he mused. This "No Man's Land" which actually belonged to many Palestinian families, all of whom Gabi knew and could name. Even the choice of name for the first Israeli checkpoint, the Mandelbaum Gate, was partial. But he decided not to dwell on the fact that the name came from the only Jewish house in the midst of an Arab neighbourhood. Perhaps the only neutral term to use was 'the 1949 Armistice Line', Gabi thought to himself.

For nineteen years (1949-1967) the Mandelbaum Gate provided the only access between the two parts of the divided city. This was where divided Palestinian families – those who remained in what became Israel and those who were forced to flee – had their annual family reunions. Yes, while families around the world had their family reunions in exciting places such as Paris, Rome, or on the lovely shores of Greece or the Caribbean islands, Palestinian family reunions took place on an Armistice Line crossing, at a checkpoint called the Mandelbaum Gate.

Gabi recalled the exchange of presents between his relatives. While Uncle Hanna and Aunt Victoria brought fresh fish from the seaport of Jaffa, Gabi's parents carried small coffee cups. As Israeli fast mud coffee slowly replaced the leisurely boiled Arabic coffee spiced with cardamom, it was becoming increasingly difficult to find the small Arabic coffee cups in the market.

Gabi realised at this point that these rowdy teenagers in the queue had been mere toddlers during the 1967 war, not to mention the 1948 one. These kids were the same age as his daughter Hania and his son Hani. Of course! It was only two days ago, June 10, that Hani had celebrated his sixteenth birthday. Gabi vividly recalled how, during the '67 war, he had had to rush his wife Haifa to a Jerusalem hospital in a bashed-up car, violating curfew in order to deliver Hani in Jerusalem so he could have a Jerusalem birth certificate.

This realisation made him see these kids in a new light; he should at least give them credit for waiting that long in line to see the new museum. Especially as none of his kids had agreed to accompany him, not even his little boy, Sami. These kids had a long wait ahead of them to learn about tolerance and co-existence.

From his fat red file Gabi pulled out a few more clippings. Ever since he had first heard of the museum and its grand opening he had started collecting all the published material he could find on the subject. He had clippings from different magazines and newspapers in Hebrew, Arabic, English, French and German, the language of Georg von Holtzbrinck, the publisher whose generous gift made this museum a reality.

As the queue started moving, Gabi's skimming through the clippings got faster, his eyes jumping from one line underlined in red to another:

"The Tourjeman Post"

The story of the period, and the history of Jerusalem as a divided city are well preserved in the Tourjeman Post. ... This house, now a museum, was once the last Israeli outpost overlooking the convoys on their way to Mt. Scopus. Some of the bullet holes in the walls still remain. The narrow, armour-plated windows are witness to nineteen years of Jordanian snipers firing at Israeli houses across the border fence.

A photo of the museum building accompanied the last review. Gabi stared at the photo and looked up. From where he was standing it was difficult to see the bullet holes; however, he clearly saw the bombarded front façade and the blown-up arches of the two balconies, as well as the cement-blocked windows.

The damage was not repaired: it was preserved by an Israeli decision as a witness ... A witness to what? Gabi wondered.

In 1948 the Hagana seized the building to use it as a forward military position.

It was used by the IDF as an observation post. ... Could this war-scarred building become a symbol of understanding?

Gabi pondered the same question.

As the queue finally started moving quickly, Gabi flipped through a few more pages:

The Museum, the first of its kind in Israel. Dedicated to dialogue, understanding and coexistence. A meeting point, a place to clarify and discuss questions concerning war, peace, conflict and reconciliation.

Gabi was getting a bit confused about the museum's name, spelled variously in different articles, and given altogether different names in others: The Tourjeman Post, The Tourjeman House, The Turjeman Position, The Tourjeman Museum, The Unification of Jerusalem Museum, The Peace Museum, Museum of Co-existence, Reconciliation Museum, and Museum on the Seam.

He knew how to spell his friend's name: Hassan *Bek* Turjman. Even though the "man" ending of the name made it sound Jewish, this Turjman was an Arab family. Perhaps that was why the Israelis opted for this name. Turjman in Arabic meant translator. But most importantly, Gabi knew well that *this* was certainly *not* a Turjman Post. And he also knew that historical accuracy was never Israel's forte.

Just before Gabi put everything back into the file to move

along with the queue, he read parts of an article written by one of the museum's former curators, Efrat Ben-Zeef:

Although it was rather obvious, it took me a while to realise that the whole idea of turning it into a museum of co-existence is naïve and impossible under the current circumstances.

Inside the new museum

Gabi could hear every step he took towards the new museum, a rhythm: boom … boom … boom … boom … for Gabi, like his father Andoni, sang bass in the Jerusalem Choir.

A numbness was stealing over his entire body as he ascended the steps of the three-arched balcony; excessive sweating spotted his elegant white shirt. He contemplated leaving the building at once. Not after this painfully long wait! he convinced himself.

A few more steps and Gabi found himself inside the entrance lobby. He felt he was drowning in the crowd of bodies, loud speeches in Hebrew emanating from speakers seeming to wash over him.

He shuddered, then froze. He felt dizzy, his eyes moving faster than his brain. His head was pounding. Not only because of the animated youngsters who were still pushing against him from behind, but also because of the loud and poor quality of the amplified Hebrew speeches and the deafening applause that followed and filled the hall. Even though he understood some Hebrew, he could hardly make out the words that were hissing from the four loudspeakers stuck high up in the lobby's four corners.

A moment of despair

His eyes rested on the balustrade of the internal staircase. He took a deep breath and allowed his eyes to travel along the railing. The two gilded letters *EA* were nicely incorporated within the beautiful wrought-iron design. Although Gabi was a chemist, he, like his late father, had an eye for architectural detail. He missed his father. Gabi gazed at the ceiling of the lobby.

He replaced the modern spotlights with a spring green and light rose Murano chandelier. He then looked to his left and changed the high tech aluminium counter for a red mahogany desk and bookcase. He took two steps to one side of the long queue and stole a quick glance at the huge hall to the right. A glass screen separated the three bay windows from the great hall. What a pity, it would have been much better if the bay windows had remained part of the great hall, flooding it with light.

He removed the round glass table inside the bay window area in favour of a set of Chippendale white and beige sofas, two red leather Art Deco chairs and a mahogany coffee table. On the coffee table were two half-filled coffee cups and a stack of *National Geographic* and *Life* magazines. One was open to a photo of a beautiful black horse, probably an Arabian.

Gabi leaned forward, catching a glimpse of the three blown-up posters hanging on the opposite wall of the same hall. He read the bold lettering on each:

Photographs of the Divided and Reunited City (1948-67)
Paintings of Jerusalem
Poems about Jerusalem

Just before he finished replacing the three posters with portraits of family members and original still-life paintings, someone tapped him on the right shoulder. "Could you get back in line?" Israelis do not have much use for the word "please". He mechanically complied. From his new position Gabi could now see another clearly legible sign:

"The Room of Vision: Hertzel and Ben-Gurion"

Why the additional "t" and "e" in Hertzel? His name was Herzl, Gabi edited mentally. It was only at this point that he realised that the loud noise filling the entrance hall had come from the "room of vision". The voice of Herzl, the father of Zionism, and the voice of Andoni, the father of both Gabi and modern architecture in Palestine, were echoing like a mixed track in his head. The "Independence of Israel Speech" by its first prime minister, David Ben-Gurion, and the echoing of the passionate words of Palestine's first architect drowned everything else.

Wedding of Gabi and Haifa Baramki

Behind the high tech aluminium ticket counter hung a huge photo of a family that could almost have been Gabi's own. To the left of a round wooden table sat a bearded man, to his left sat a woman, probably his wife, in a stylish white dress. Their two children, dressed elegantly, stood behind, the boy leaning against the table, the girl standing behind her dad.

Herzl and his family, c. 1866-1873

Gabi gazed at Herzl's family photo. No wonder they won the world's sympathy, they reflect so many human faces from countless family photo albums.

Gabi remembered the family albums left behind. He looked around frantically.

A moment of cold terror

At the ticket counter

"How many tickets? One?" inquired the young woman sitting behind the high-tech aluminium counter.

"Tickets?" Gabi exclaimed, absentmindedly.

"Yes, tickets!" smiled back the ticket vendor.

"Tickets?" Gabi repeated.

"Yes, sir, tickets." She smiled again, then cautiously asked, "Senior?"

"Senior?" Gabi's face broke into a broad smile as he added, "Perhaps too senior, exceedingly senior!"

"*Come on ...* For God's sake, hurry up, buy the bloody ticket and move on!" complained a young voice behind him.

For a fraction of a second Gabi looked back, then turned and gazed at the ticket woman for long moments.

"Did you say I should buy a ticket?" Gabi came back to his theme.

"Yes, sir. This is not a free museum, you *must* buy a ticket, I do not understand the problem." She was perplexed, a little annoyed.

"*Must*! Indeed. And how much is the ticket?" Gabi seemed to ponder this deeply, the smile continuing to spread across his face.

"Thirty shekels regular, twenty-five for seniors."

"Thirty shekels regular, twenty-five for seniors," Gabi repeated.

The ticket woman lost her temper. "What is the matter with

you, sir? Today is the museum's opening, and as you can see we have tons of visitors waiting in line." She rolled her eyes and sighed.

"Yes, yes, of course, what is the matter with me?" Gabi responded, his smile slowly turning into hysterical laughter. "Hahaha, hahaha, hahaha … hahaha … hahaha …!"

"For fuck's sake, something is seriously wrong with this man, would someone get him out of the queue? How much longer are we expected to wait?" The complaints from the line behind him were getting louder and angrier.

"You want me to pay thirty shekels to enter … hahaha … my hahaha … this is … Hahaha … my hahaha … ha hahaha …" Gabi's attempts at speech were foiled by hysterical laughter. People stood there, watching nervously.

Gabi gave it another try. "Do you *really* want me to pay thirty Israeli shekels to enter my hou … hahaha … my family hou … hahaha … The Baramki hou … hahaha, my father, Andoni, … Baramki … hahaha … hahaha …"

No one around him could figure out what he was trying to say.

"*Mazeh*? I do not understand what is going on here, sir." The ticket clerk made one last attempt.

Gabi's obscure words were transformed into nervous howls: as loud and as deafening as those of Herzl and Ben-Gurion's Independence Day speeches.

He chuckled and laughed, then bent over clutching his stomach.

"I think he is saying this is his family's house!"

A moment of silence

The ticket girl ducked down
Some froze
Some cautiously moved away
Some ran out

Some opted to shut their eyes
But the vast majority closed their ears and carried on with
their lives
Business as usual
Life as normal
They acted like they were normal people in a normal
country.

Gabi's laughter first filled the entrance hall, soon after travelled to the guest quarters, to the dining room, then to the huge kitchen. It made its way to the family room upstairs, into his parents' bedroom, his sister Laura's pink bedroom, to his brother George's blue room and finally into his own. The laughter went into every drawer and into the corners of the closets in his room, but the photo albums were nowhere in sight.

To this day, museum visitors feel the reverberation of joyless laughter in the air.

A true account of the museum

From April 28, 1948, when the Baramkis left their home, until the grand opening of the Tourjeman Post Museum on June 12, 1983 – for thirty-six years, that is – none of the Baramkis had been able to set foot in their own house.

George Baramki, Gabi's younger brother, had actually accompanied him that day. However their father, Andoni, the architect who had passed away eleven years earlier (in September 1972) was never allowed in, hence he never saw "the light of his life" again from the inside. Evelyn, his wife and Gabi and George's mother, in whose name the house was registered, and their sister Laura could never stand in that "museum" queue. Their tears would have flooded the whole of the Holy Land.

It was also reported that the sponsor of the museum, Georg von Holtzbrinck, had died in Germany on the night of the grand opening of the 'Tourjeman Post Museum'.

Part Three

Huda

Peace – that was another name for home.

Kathleen Norris

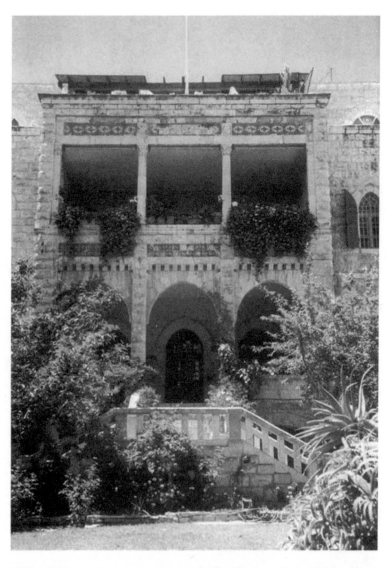

Villa Bisharat, better known as Villa Harun al-Rashid, where Israeli Prime Minister, Golda Meir, lived. Talbiyeh, January, c. 1928.

4

Golda Slept Here

It was a beautiful spring day in Jerusalem. And the very last thing that the two elegantly dressed bourgeois ladies and I expected, on an outing on a spring-like day, was that one of us would be arrested, handcuffed, and thrown into prison.

Nahil, eighty-seven, is Huda's older cousin. She had just arrived in Jerusalem from Damascus, via Amman and across the Allenby Bridge.

Hurriedly, Nahil checked into the American Colony Hotel, by far the most charming and most expensive hotel in East Jerusalem. She could have taken time to freshen up, relax, have a nice cup of Turkish coffee, or even a drink in the hotel's splendid courtyard, but she did not. Instead she opted to rush to her cousin's office in the Old City of Jerusalem. Attractive and wild-looking Huda was surprised and delighted to see her older cousin. The two exchanged many warm kisses.

"Sorry, habibti Huda, I didn't mean to descend on you like qadar, fate, without warning, but the second Samir told me that our German Colony house was no longer occupied by the Jewish school, I came running." There was a nervy silence before Nahil added, "Imagine, today could be *the day* when I'll set foot inside our house again. I haven't been in it since I left in 1947. I vividly recall that day as if it were yesterday: It was

September 13, a brisk and sunny day. I was so excited to get to my university in Damascus, I hadn't the slightest inkling that I'd never be able to come back home again."

Nahil's eyes had a far-away look in them, as if she was already home.

Attempting to calm down her highly anxious and emotional cousin, Huda smiled and spoke in a very comforting tone: "Relax, habibti, we'll go and see it right away. Your brother Samir is right; it's no longer a school so there's no guard to prevent you from going in. It's now a construction site and will remain so for a while. I've already been there a number of times. I don't know if Samir told you, but Amidar[4] has put the whole compound up for sale: yours, Uncle Subhi's, and Teta Aysheh's."

What a strange way to lower Nahil's high anxiety, I thought to myself.

"Up for sale?" Nahil was in total shock. She slapped the sides of her head with both hands while her jaw dropped. She collapsed into a chair and stared blankly for a long time. When she came to herself she asked in a broken, shaky voice, "And has Amidar already sold our houses?"

"I don't think so, habibti. I was there two weeks ago. Though the important thing for now is for you to get inside the house." Huda seemed to regret having given Nahil such bad news.

Nahil decided to focus on the good news for now. "Ok, let's go." They both rose from their chairs.

Since Huda was leaving work earlier than usual, she stacked her papers and then forced them into her soft leather black handbag.

Clickety-click, clickety-click…

Huda strode energetically down the corridor, swaying left and right, her high heels announcing the departure of the

---

[4] Amidar is the Israeli government agency entrusted with Arab absentee properties.

Director of the Centre for Jerusalem Studies at Al-Quds University. The domes of the renovated Turkish hammam seemed to amplify, rather than absorb, the sound of Huda's footsteps.

She was as elegant as usual in her short grey skirt, black tights planted into high-heel boots, and a skin-tight grey blouse over which hung a burgundy shawl. Huda always looked like she was on her way to one of the many receptions held by one or the other of the diplomatic missions in Jerusalem.[5] In fact, she often went to the French Consulate where her son Hani works. Both Huda and her son carry French passports acquired through Huda's previous marriage to a man from Martinique. Perhaps that was one source of Huda's incredible courage, verging on recklessness, in facing life in general and Israeli soldiers and authorities in particular.

Huda's fluffed, light-brown curls framed an ever-smiling face sitting atop an animated physique that radiated a confident personality and an attitude of entitlement. This makes her pass for a coquettish Frenchwoman, which no doubt helps her deceive almost all soldiers manning Jerusalem's three major checkpoints: Qalandia, Beit Jala Tunnel, and Hizma. She had managed to sneak me in 'illegally' through one of them the night before.

Nothing energises vivacious Huda more than a planned (or even better, a spontaneous) visit to an Arab house in what was once a majority Arab neighbourhood in West Jerusalem, especially if the visit is to her own family house, not far from Nahil's, in the elegant Greek Colony.

Hardly a week passes without Huda venturing on such a visit, either alone or with her mother, her son Hani (when he

---

[5] Of all the pre-1948 diplomatic missions in Jerusalem, fourteen continue to function in both parts of the divided city. After the creation of Israel in 1948, Tel Aviv was declared its capital and new embassies opened there. After 1994 and the creation of the Palestinian National Authority, new missions opened in Ramallah.

was younger and she could drag him along), or any other willing family member. She often takes along friends, journalists, or TV reporters. In fact she has been seen leading busloads of alternative tourists. Whenever she does this Huda runs the risk of having the Jewish family living in her house report her to the police, who come running to their 'rescue'.

Invariably, Huda's energy and excitement lead her companions to think that this was the very *first time* she had ventured to visit Arab homes and neighbourhoods in West Jerusalem. However, her facial expressions, neurotic energy, and the frequency of her nervous laughter indicate to the keen observer the deep exhaustion resulting from an addiction bordering on *obsession*.

Yes, an obsession

Like most Palestinians, Huda is haunted by the past and tortured by the unfairness of the present.

Soon, Nahil and I were with our guide on one of her many personally guided tours. These are not to be confused with the public tours organised by her organisation: the Jerusalem Studies Centre (www.Jerusalem-studiestours.com). Huda's personally guided tours have included the following:

1. Whose House is this One?
2. The Market Value of Your House Today
3. The Biggest Real Estate Robbery in Recent History
4. Everything You Want to Know about the Family that Lives in Your House
5. Golda Slept Here
6. Nakba Survivals: an annual peaceful march to Arab neighbourhoods with the owners of these houses (whose main organiser was Huda's friend, Mona Halabi) and many others.

66

How I wish I could sneak into Jerusalem more frequently to take them all. However this time I was on a specific mission: to meet, accompany, and interview the protagonists of this book.

"Here is Mamilla Cemetery,[6] this is where my grandfather, Jamal al-Imam was buried. I don't know how much longer we can protect his bones and the bones of all the others, before the Israelis bulldoze the whole cemetery. Their Jewish bones are sacred, but ours *al-zbaleh*, off to the rubbish heap," Huda said from behind the wheel as she pointed with her right arm, almost hitting Nahil's nose. I was sitting quietly in the back seat.

And since my mission for the day was to deal with Jewish families *living* in Arab houses, I decided to 'let the dead bury their dead', at least for now.

"Suad, see that beautiful three-arch building over there? That also belongs to Nahil's family. The Israelis are turning it into a five-star hotel." I could hear Nahil sigh. I glanced at the beautiful building from the rear window. I could easily imagine it as a luxury hotel. I wanted to ask if they knew who the architect was (as I suspected, it turned out to be Andoni Baramki), but then decided it was not the right moment and kept quiet.

But soon the architect in me surfaced again as we passed the peculiar neo-Byzantine style stone building of the YMCA. "You know, the YMCA building was designed by the same architect who did the Empire State Building, Arthur Loomis Harmon," I offered excitedly, but got no reaction. They couldn't care less.

I was looking outside the window when Huda pointedly said, "Suad, this was the Palestine Broadcasting building; this is

---

[6] "On July 12, 2011, the Israeli Interior Ministry approved construction plans for the Museum of Tolerance, allowing construction to begin immediately. On July 21, 45 distinguished Palestinian community leaders urged the UN High Commissioner for Human Rights and the Director-General of UNESCO to immediately intervene to stop the desecration of the cemetery. The Center for Constitutional Rights, a US non-profit organisation, and the Campaign continue to advocate for the preservation of this historic and sacred site." www.mamillacampaign.org.

where your Baba and Bayan's father, Ajaj Nuwayhid, worked. By the way, did you see the new film, *Huna Al Quds* (Jerusalem Calling)?

This got my full attention. "Unfortunately, I wasn't able to. I was away when they screened it in Ramallah recently. Friends who saw it told me I look like my Baba."

"A carbon copy," Huda said, laughing.

I giggled as I thought how some, like Umm Samir's daughter, tell me I look so much like my mother, and others, like Huda, tell me I am a carbon copy of my father. My mother and father were not sister and brother!

I went back to trying to be the invisible presence on this trip. While my eyes were busy skipping from one splendid villa to the next in those gorgeous neighbourhoods, it was easy to keep quiet. I was listening attentively to every single word Huda and Nahil uttered, though they were mostly Huda's. The one thing that I thought I was sure of was that I did not want this trip to be about me, or about my parents, since they too had lost their livelihood and their home.

But in a strange way it was about them.

I did not want to admit to myself or to any of the displaced Palestinians who appear in this book that, emotionally taxing as these visits and conversations were, to me they were therapy sessions. And as we all know, therapy sessions are often more painful than the pain they seek to alleviate.

The agonies and pain I felt as I accompanied my protagonists made me realise that neither my body nor my soul were prepared to dig up my family's story in Jaffa.

I had buried deep *the heavy burden of the past* and the unbearable darkness enveloping the tragic events of 1948. Perhaps this explained my admiration for Huda's unwavering persistence.

Huda was actively incensed while I, like many others, plunged into silent gloom.

My reflections halted when Huda unexpectedly slammed on the brakes. By the time I swung my head away from the window I was gazing through she was already outside the car, pointing to the right: "Nahil, Suad, look, look at this: *Golda slept here!*"

"*Golda slept here!*" I repeated, then asked, "What do you mean, Golda slept here?"

"Golda Meir, right?" Nahil wanted to make sure.

"Yes, habibti, Golda Meir lived in an Arab house." Nahil and I peered out of the window. Huda continued:

"Nahil, habibti, I know how anxious you are to get to your own house, I promise this won't take long. Come on, you two, get out of the car." Huda had parked in the middle of the road, her door wide open. She ran across the road and stood in front of a gorgeous three-storey villa. The size of the structure made me think it must be a school, or a hotel.

"Now look at the ceramic tiles on the second-floor frieze, can you read?" Huda was in schoolteacher mode. I struggled to read the damaged navy-blue Arabic calligraphy on the white ceramic tiles.

"Villa Harun al-Rashid," Nahil read out loud. With her excellent Damascene Arabic she was able to decipher the defaced Arabic writing long before I could.

"Yes, Golda Meir lived in the Villa Harun al-Rashid[7] in the 1960s. And when the UN Secretary General, Dag Hammarskjöld came to visit 'her' villa, she made sure to sandblast the Arabic script to conceal the fact that she, the prime minister of Israel, was living in an Arab house. And do you know whose villa this really *is?*" Huda never uses the past tense when it comes to Palestinian ownership of properties in Jerusalem or Israel.

---

[7] Harun al-Rahsid was a ninth-century Abbasid Caliph in Baghdad known for his wise rule, great wealth, and interest in promoting cultural and intellectual growth.

The only person I could think of was Edward Said, as Talbiyeh, where we were, was his neighbourhood.

"No, habibti, this is not Edward's house, but we'll soon pass by it and see the monstrous new building that's been built over the Said house. Villa Harun al-Rashid belongs to George Bisharat's family.

Oh, George's![8] How beautiful.

Asmahan dined here

Huda parked her car right across the Aweidah compound. She made sure to pay the parking fee for the anticipated one-hour stay. Considering the nature of our visit, it would be absolutely silly to be stopped by the police for a parking violation.

The mundane things one has to do in life!

Using the back alley, the two elegantly dressed ladies cautiously entered the rundown garden of their huge compound. I followed.

Indeed, the compound was no longer used as a school, but somehow it looked more deserted than the active construction site that Huda had mentioned. Despite its desolation, or perhaps because of it, both of them, especially Nahil, looked like intruders.

Their animated talk as well as their high energy levels gave way to timid and nervous movements in no time. Even though this was Nahil's family compound I could sense that she was uncomfortable while walking through it: she was overly cautious and apprehensive, as if she were trespassing on someone else's property.

It is the occupation of the mind and the emotions that scares me most.

---

[8] See George Bisharat's article about visiting his own house, "Talbiyeh Days: At Villa Harun al-Rashid in Jerusalem" in *Jerusalem Quarterly* 30: Vol. 8, No 2. Spring 2007, pp. 88-98.

But this was Nahil's home, this was where she grew up, where she played with the other children in her neighbourhood, where she went to school; this was where she met her first love, and this is where her extended family lived.

As for Huda, this was her grandmother Aysheh's house. This is where Teta Aysheh lived before she got married and was 'demoted' by going to live with her in-laws in Jerusalem's Old City.

Huda's grandmother's tales about the rich life and splendour of this compound instigated her frequent visits. The obsession had started when she visited the house as a child for the very first time right after the '67 war. Meanwhile Nahil, in the course of her sixty-three-year absence (1947-2011) in Damascus, had nurtured her childhood and adolescent memories from afar.

While Huda felt very much at home, everything about Nahil conveyed a strong sense of estrangement. Together, but also separately, they meandered in what was once a lavish garden and through the narrow paths between the two houses. They stopped here and there: touching this plant and staring at that stone. They poked their heads through this window and that.

I could easily imagine how high Nahil's adrenalin levels must have been in anticipation of a confrontation with an Israeli guard or *any* Israeli who might suddenly appear. I could imagine the fights and arguments between her family spirits and the spectres of the Israeli users of her property. They seemed to be taking place inside her head. They probably also involved an argument with Amidar, the Israeli agency that is 'entrusted' with her property, as well as all other Palestinian 'absentee properties'.

Soon Nahil stood in front of a huge fig tree, placed her palm on its cracked and coarse bark and slowly raised her head: yes, she remembered. "This must be the same fig tree behind which I hid when I played hide-and-seek with my siblings and cousins," she murmured to herself.

Nahil continued her melancholic ramblings on a huge concrete slab which had been poured over the lavish garden that once separated the two identical houses from the main street. She looked up at the three suffocating Aleppo pines and felt herself suffocating too.

Having explored every nook and cranny at the back, in the gardens and all the narrow paths, Nahil finally arrived at the front entrance to her house where Huda and I were standing.

The three of us stood in front of the two magnificent houses located on the busy Bethlehem Road (now Emek Refaim). My architect's eyes moved quickly between the two identical houses. It did not take long for me to figure out that one was a mirror image of the other. The one to the left belongs to Nahil's father, and the one on the right to Huda's grandmother.

I could tell that the beautiful pink stone of the main elevations was brought from the famous *slayyeb* quarry of the neighbouring village of Beit Fajjar. *Slayyeb*, a very expensive stone, literally means the hard and impermeable.

From the outside, I could also guess that both houses were typical of what architects call the liwan-house layout: one or two elongated living spaces in the middle with two or three rooms on each side – a total of six or eight spaces with a staircase to the side of the house.

The elevated one-floor houses had pitched roofs with red Marseilles tiles, also typical of the British Mandate Period (1921-1948). The most beautiful architectural details were the five huge arches of the front façades. Their bright white stones contrasted beautifully with the pink, even eighty years after they had been built. While the middle entrance arch was wide and flat, the two arches on either side were of the same height, but narrow and pointed.

Sadly, what were once very large glass windows overlooking a lavish front garden had become small windows with iron bars overlooking a huge expanse of concrete. And yet the Israelis claim they made the desert bloom. I kept the thought to myself as I looked at the cement walls that blocked the five arches and at the huge cement slab.

Nahil and Huda's unexpected giggles interrupted my musings: they had left me to my endless architectural obsessions. I looked in their direction. Huda was taking a series of photographs while Nahil held an intriguing pose: standing on one leg while stretching the other over the slanting parapet that flanked the stairs leading to her house.

"As kids we loved sliding on this smooth stone parapet." Nahil carefully balanced herself as she smiled for the camera. I could see the mood had changed. Nice.

I prayed that Nahil would not slide down that parapet. Her one-legged pose was dangerous enough for a woman of seventy-eight. But thankfully she seemed to know her limits: once done with nostalgic acrobatics she carefully climbed the seven steps leading to the front veranda.

Nahil moved between the two windows flanking the main entrance. She pressed her head against the iron bars of one window and then placed her two arms around her head to shield her eyes against the glare. She was trying hard to peer inside her home.

Meanwhile Huda had gripped the handle of the main door, and, exerting all her strength and body weight, managed to turn it. To her surprise the heavy cast-iron door gave way. She looked at Nahil and smiled. Nahil did not reciprocate. She took one step in the direction of the half-open door, looked inside the house, and froze.

Like a bronze statue she froze.

I had tears in my eyes.

The interior of the house was flooded with the light of the melancholic afternoon sun. Parts of what was once the living room liwan could now be seen. Huda slipped her thin body through the gap between Nahil's bronze statue and the rusty cast-iron door. Nahil's stiff body quietly followed suit, and so did I.

There was silence.

Utter silence until Nahil's loud sobs echoed through the whole house.

"See how beautiful these tiles are!" Huda attempted to break the awkwardness of the situation. They looked at one another and smiled. Huda came close to her elder cousin and hugged her tightly. "Yes," she said, "like everything else in this house, they are truly gorgeous."

Silence prevailed once more.

"Let me see if I can get some water to splash onto the tiles so that we can see their beautiful colours," Huda said, stepping out of the house in search of water and escaping the throat-constricting situation.

Soon Nahil's eyes reflected that she was slipping into the past. I could now see that she was a child hopping around her house:

She ran to her bedroom and threw her school bag, and then her small body, onto the bed. She loved that bounce. Her sister Lamis was already at her desk, studying. Nahil resented Lamis's good study habits, which often resulted in their mother Husniyeh demanding similar behaviour of Nahil; while all Nahil wanted to do was to run out of the house to play with the neighbourhood children.

Nahil left her sister in peace and followed her nose to the kitchen. The aroma of her favourite dish filled the house. She tiptoed closer to the stove and quietly lifted the heavy cover of the huge copper pot and noiselessly put it aside. Not wanting to lose time or risk making a sound by opening the drawer to get a fork, she picked up a stuffed squash and a rolled grape vine leaf with her bare fingers. Before she managed to finish

74

swallowing the burning hot squash, she heard her mother's reprimand. "Nahil? Is that you in the kitchen? Please do not eat on your own, wait for your father. He is on his way home, soon we will all have lunch together." But Nahil knew better. Baba never came home on time. He was always in his travel agency trying to satisfy his customers. So she kept at it, grabbing more rolled vine leaves. Mmmm, yummy. She licked her fingers.

Nahil was soon caught red-handed, quite literally. She was cooling her burnt tongue with a cold glass of water when her mother stepped into the kitchen.

"Stop it, Nahil! Please go to your room, or better, leave your sister alone. Go to your father's study and do your homework."

"Why start now if Baba is on his way home?"

Both knew that Adel would be late, but they still kept it up. "Habibti Nahil, do not argue with me now, just go and do your homework."

Nahil walked out of the kitchen, through the living room and out to the front balcony. She mounted the sloping stone parapet of the staircase and zooooom, slid down. She ran through the back garden just in time to see the train as it passed on its way from Jerusalem to Jaffa. Often, together with the neighbourhood kids, Nahil would excitedly wait for the train to pass and flatten the nails they had just placed on the tracks. "Heeeeey," Nahil and her friends jubilated while their shrieks accompanied the train as it travelled between the two cities.

"Here, I managed to get you some water," Huda announced as she poured it over the floor. "Wow, look! Look how pretty they are, a bit like our tiles in the Greek Colony house."

Nahil was still gobbling up her mother's yummy stuffed grape leaves. As the water splashed down, revealing the splendid colours and shapes of the living room tiles, her memory took her on another flashback:

It was going to be the first time that Asmahan's mother visited

75

them after the traumatic death of her daughter. Asmahan, the famous Lebanese singer who had just died in July 1944 in a suspicious car accident, and her mother, were good friends of the family. At the age of fourteen, Nahil shared in the havoc and hard work that preceded this famous visit.

Everyone in the compound was elegantly dressed, every single one: family members, women and men alike, and all the children; all the compound housemaids, the gardener, the driver, the cooks, and the waiters who had been hired for this special occasion. Like the two adjacent houses of her father and his brother, Nahil and her sister were dressed identically: two bright purple dresses with matching head ribbons and belts.

Every corner of the twin houses was scrubbed clean and in tiptop shape: "Clean this corner just in case!" Nahil's mother Husniyeh kept saying as she frantically went around her house giving orders and bossing over everyone.

The big salon with the newly acquired Louis XVI furniture was kept open all day long. "Kids, don't go in there," Nahil's mother's instructions to stay away from the fancy furniture were repeated frequently that day. Like everyone around her, Nahil lent a hand. She carefully carried the silverware and helped in placing it on both sides of the blue and white china plates. "No! Kids stay away from the main dining table, do not touch those crystal glasses, you can only help in preparing your table, the kids' table," her mother kept saying to her little nephews and nieces.

Being fourteen, Nahil hoped she would be placed at the same table with the guest of honour, Asmahan's mother. If love of Asmahan's songs was to determine the seating arrangement, Nahil's place would be right next to Asmahan's mother. But Nahil knew better than to hope, even though she loved Asmahan much more than she loved Umm Kulthum, Asmahan's chief rival.

It was Teta Aysheh who announced that Asmahan's mother had arrived. In no time everyone was standing in their assigned places in the long welcoming queue: grandmother, aunts, uncles, grandfathers, even young cousins, everyone had a place. Nahil will never forget the elegant lady who walked in: tall and blonde, wearing a tight black dress, a long black fur stole and graceful high heels. No one in Jerusalem was as elegant as this Egyptian-Lebanese lady. She looked like a queen. The Queen was soon escorted to the sacred salon and the kids were instructed to disappear until lunch was served. Nahil settled down next to her sister in the living room. They positioned themselves where they could see the Queen in the Louis XVI salon.

When lunch was announced they all followed the Queen and Teta Aysheh into the dining room. While waiting for everyone to be seated, Nahil was delighted to discover that the last two seats at the main table were for her and her older sister, Lamis. As she threw her body onto the dream-come-true chair Nahil was instantly instructed by her mother to sit up straight, keep quiet and observe the rules of etiquette. With shaky hands she picked up the fork and knife and elegantly ate her stuffed squash and rolled stuffed grape leaves. Stealing continuous glances in the direction of Asmahan's mother, she swore to God that the stuffed grape leaves tasted much better when picked right out of the burning hot pot in her mother's kitchen.

Ending Asmahan's mother's visit to the house abruptly, Huda called out: "Nahil, Suad, let's get going. We need to get to our Greek Colony house before it gets dark."

As we walked out of the compound Nahil went close to a window shutter. She leaned forward and grabbed a rusted cast-iron stopper in the shape of a woman's bust which was fixed into a stone windowsill.

"This is my bedroom," Nahil panted, as she pulled and jiggled the woman's bust. She pulled as hard as her aging muscles could. When she failed to get it out Huda tried, but the tenacious and rusty old woman refused to leave home.

They left her alone and walked away empty-handed.

On the Jerusalem-Jaffa railroad tracks

Soon the three of us were walking on the wooden pavement which covers the old railroad tracks that once served as an infinite playground for Nahil and her friends. Something about these tracks seems to have haunted the neighbourhood children and grown-ups alike. The power of the passing train, as well as its whistle and steam, constituted one vivid image that they carried with them into Diaspora.

"It was on these railway tracks that Bayan, Mona and I spent the best days of our childhood," Nahil said as the three of us walked along the narrow and endless path. "We would place a few nails on the tracks and wait for the train to pass. When the driver saw us he would jokingly release the steam from a safe distance. Twisting and turning our bodies, we would laugh and giggle. But soon after, we would happily proceed to our nearby school."

I noted that the little Jerusalemite girls placed nails, rather than coins, on the tracks; this made me think that my mother's accusation of Jerusalemites being tightfisted had some truth to it.

Moved by the three little girls' flirtatious episode I was delighted that Mona was a friend, while Bayan was the daughter of one of my father's friends. This anchored me somehow and helped reduce the strong sense of estrangement that had accompanied me on this visit.

Lost in Nahil's and Huda's endless list of who owned what in this lost Arab neighbourhood, I gazed west in the direction of the infinite tracks and eventually found myself on the train, being carried from Jerusalem to *my* family home in Jaffa.

My journey from Jerusalem to Jaffa must have taken an hour or so. As I often do on trains I watched the beautiful landscape go by. From Batir's bright lettuce-green plains to the dusty olive-green of Ein Karem's rocky valley. And once the scent of orange blossom reached me I knew it was time to stand up and get ready to get off the train. I stretched my legs as I waited for the train to come to a complete stop, and only then did I jump off the elevated carriage onto the narrow platform at al Manshieh Station, our neighbourhood. And in less than five minutes I was home, having lunch on the terrace and looking out at the agitated Mediterranean sea.

I must admit that this was the very first time that I had gathered the courage to go back to my father's house on the seashores of Jaffa. It must have been Huda's karma.

My daydream came to an end as I heard Nahil whisper, "Yes, yes, this *is* Mona and Bayan's house. Look, look at the Israeli family sitting around enjoying Bayan's balcony."

5

Whose House is This?

"Hello there!" I yelled at the top of my voice, addressing a chubby, half-bald, middle-aged man standing on a second-floor balcony.

The garden, in the middle of which stood the two-storey house, was absolutely delightful. The old pine and cypress trees around the house, as well as the architectural style and details, made me think it must have been built sometime in the 1930s.

I may not be jealous of people with big luxurious houses but I am certainly envious, and in this case resentful, of people with such luxuriant thriving gardens.

"Hi?" He answered back questioningly in an equally friendly and cordial manner. He walked around the table in the middle of the large balcony and came closer to the balustrade. The two people sitting right behind him, a woman and a young girl, carried on chatting indifferently.

They were acting as if they were normal people in a normal country.

Huda, who was standing next to me, giggled, while Nahil stiffened.

The lightness and friendliness in my voice and his, as well as Huda's cheerfulness, made me realise what a spring-like day in November could do to people's spirits.

80

The luminous pink stone surface of the main façade of this gorgeous house not only reflected Jerusalem's splendid autumn light, it almost reflected the shades and shadows as well as the bright *and* dark spots in my heart, Huda's, and certainly Nahil's.

"Yes? How can I help you?" asked the balcony-man as he leaned forward across the balustrade in a welcoming gesture.

"Hi, how are you?" I greeted him nervously once more, as if I had just encountered a lost cousin, not a lost house.

"What can I do for you?" the balcony man, perplexed, also repeated his question.

"We *only* want you to give back the house to its Arab owners," whispered Huda, cracking her typical loud laugh.

"Shush, stop it Huda!" I nudged her with my elbow and swiftly turned my full attention to the balcony-man. I did not want to lose this rare instance of a kind and accommodating Israeli.

"Do you live here?" What a dumb question, of course he does.

"Ye-e-e-s, why?" he answered, drawing out the vowel.

"I need to ask you something," I said.

The balcony man was getting curious, as were the two others, probably his wife and young daughter. They too came closer to the edge of the balcony. The three exchanged looks and a few words before the balcony-man yelled back: "Coming!"

My heart skipped a beat. Astounded, I asked, "Did you hear what he said?"

"Don't worry, Suad, we can handle him," Huda gave me a reassuring smile then added, "but let's act dumb."

"In my case, no need to act." I wasn't sure I was ready for this encounter.

"I can't possibly take this, not now and certainly not today," said an agitated Nahil as she walked away from us. "Sorry ladies, I'll wait for you at home."

I was truly sorry to lose Nahil, the only one among us who grew up in this neighbourhood and knew every single house and each and every owner, first-hand. But there was no time to mourn her sudden departure.

Since I had spontaneously and unintentionally (perhaps also irresponsibly) initiated this encounter with one of the many Israelis residing in Arab homes, I felt the need to be better prepared before we came face to face with the tenant or the "owner" of Mona and Bayan's homes.

Desperate, I sought Huda's help. "So, quickly, before he arrives, the downstairs belonged to Mona's grandfather, Adel Jaber, and the upstairs to Ajaj Nuwayhid, Bayan's father, right?"

With Huda saying I got it right the balcony-man appeared. My heart skipped a beat.

"Hello, how can I help you?" he asked in a curious but polite manner – or as polite as an Israeli can be. He seemed self-assured and happy. Of course, I too would be as happy and as smug if I were given a house like this.

Face to face with the balcony-man, my anxiety vanished. Up close he looked younger and less formidable. I was getting extremely uncomfortable and irritated by the normality and sweetness of the encounter, but Huda made sure this didn't last long.

"Whose house is this?" she asked, right up front.

Since I was intending to write about this encounter, I did not want it to end too quickly. I posed the same question in a less confrontational manner. "Is this your house?" I asked.

"Yes," he confirmed, a bit bewildered.

"A lovely house and a most beautiful garden," Huda said, a sly smile spreading over her not–so–innocent face.

"Yes … but the garden isn't mine, I live on the second floor," meaning as far as the garden was concerned, he wasn't guilty.

"Do you want to sell your house?" Huda was at him again.

82

"Because I am looking for a house for my ..." But she was swiftly interrupted.

"No … no, of course not, why would I sell it?" he replied in an utterly dismissive manner.

"I am looking for an Arab house to buy or rent for my son, Mohammad." I could not help but giggle to hear Huda change her son's name from Hani to Mohammad.

He was obviously growing ill at ease talking to these not-so-innocent two women, but he remained courteous.

"Isn't this the house of Adel Jaber?" Huda asked, keeping a straight face.

"I don't know," he replied calmly.

"You *don't know*!!"

As Huda got angry he tried to modify his response. "Well, not so long ago, some people from Canada …"

"From San Francisco," I felt a strong urge to correct him even though it did not really matter whether Mona had come from Canada or San Francisco. I must say I was also irritated by his use of the expression "some people".

If the Israelis have been so indifferent, or even happy, as to throw out 850,000 Palestinians from their homes, the least they can do is to show some respect or a bit of sensitivity by knowing the name of the family in whose house they are living now!

As my anger mounted he continued: "Some people [meaning Mona] came here a few years ago: they wanted to see the house where they lived before the War of Independence. I let them in, they took some photographs, and went away."

End of story.

They went away when they should have stayed; they should have entered their homes and stayed there, I thought to myself. His mentioning the "War of Independence" also got to me. I have never understood why the Israelis call the 1948 Nakba, our catastrophe, the War of Independence. Independence from

83

whom? From the British, who helped them set up a Jewish State in historic Palestine? Or even more absurd, independence from us Palestinians?

While I was fuming, veteran Huda and the balcony-man kept at it: "Yes, I think it was a woman, but I don't remember her name," he claimed, or at best did not care to remember.

"Her name is Mona; she is a *very* close friend of ours," Huda got specific. Like me, the total denial was getting to her.

"But she told me it was *not* her house, she rented it from somebody."

"And do you know *who* that body is?" Huda was gradually revealing her knowledge of every Arab house and every Arab owner.

"I don't know."

"And would you care to know in whose house you and your family are living now?" Huda's tone was turning nasty.

"The owner of my house never lived in it."

"So, you got to know that he did not live in it, but you do not know his name?"

"No, I don't know his name."

"Well, sir, the owner of this building is Mr. Hazboun, a very rich merchant from a very well-known Bethlehem family, and the tenant in whose house you are living right now is Mr. Ajaj Nuwayhid. Professor Bayan, his daughter, happens to be a very good friend of ours. And do you have any idea who these people are?"

"No."

I stood there and wondered if the balcony-man truly did not know that Bayan's husband was the prominent PLO activist and intellectual, Shafiq al-Hout.

I could not believe that he did not care to know the name of the owner or the tenant of "his" house, the very house on whose balcony he and his family were now sitting and enjoying the cool autumn afternoon.

I stood there wondering about the total denial that underlay his lack of interest in who had lived there, who was kicked out from there, and who was prevented from going back. She came, took some photos and went away … end of story for him.

I wondered about the ability to simply not go there.

In spite of my anger I was still curious about how he got to live in a house that was privately owned by the Hazboun family, who were never compensated for it. Contemplating the magnitude of the tragedy and the enormity of the absentee property and ownership laws whereby a whole country was stolen, I had no wish to continue to be personal with this rare and relatively accommodating Israeli who stood there, willing to give and take (give only in words, of course). So I tried to ask some more general questions.

"By the way, what happened to the property of the Palestinians? I mean the houses they *own*?" I, like Huda, purposely did not use the past tense. "The houses in which they lived before 1948? Are they still under the control of the Israeli government or have they been privatised?"

"No, they're still with Amidar, the Israeli government agency. They have sold some and are in the process of selling more, that is how I bought my house."

I was getting extremely angry at his use of the expression "my house". Huda was also getting personal and emotionally charged.

"Oh yes, the infamous Amidar, who in 1997 sold our Greek Colony villa to Udi Kaplan, the Israeli real estate agency, when I could not get it back or even buy it just because I am Palestinian. He bought it, restored it, added an ugly triangular penthouse on top of it, and sold it for three and a half million dollars."

"*Three and a half million dollars, wow!*" I couldn't but repeat with a sigh.

"Yes, Suad, I am potentially a millionaire, all I need to do at this point is to convert to Judaism."

"Why don't we *all* convert to Judaism? If a million Russians, half of whom were Greek Orthodox, migrated to Israel claiming they were Jewish, why shouldn't we be able to do the same?" I added to Huda's brilliant idea.

"It should be much easier, since half of us are already circumcised," Huda broke into hysterical laughter while the balcony-man and I blushed. Still, I could see that the balcony-man found the circumcision joke entertaining in an unsettling way.

"Yes, prices are going up all the time. Come on, ladies, be serious, all I can tell you at this point is, go talk to your lawyer … because it is *very, very* complicated." The balcony-man found it less painful to talk about property prices than circumcision.

"Bye," he turned around and walked home.

"Bye," we turned in the opposite direction and walked along the infinite train tracks.

And that is when I heard Huda mumbling to herself in an Israeli accent: "'Come on, ladies, be seghious, go talk to yough lawyegh,' because it is all a *very very well-executed theft.*"

That same afternoon.

Huda could have easily parked her navy blue Golf right next to her family house, but she did not.

Neither Nahil nor I noticed that she had purposely parked it around the corner, further up the road from her house at 18 Uzia Street, as it is now called. "I have no clue who Uzia is, or what Uzia means," Huda replied dismissively when Nahil enquired.

Cunning Huda did not want to reveal the risks we, and most particularly she, were taking by visiting her family house. Her rooster-like walk and utter confidence made me feel relaxed and reassured. The normality of the situation led me to believe that we were going to have a drink under the trees in their lush green garden, followed by dinner on their big terrace, exactly like the Jewish family we had just left sitting on Bayan's balcony.

"Here we are in the Greek Colony neighbourhood, see how charming and peaceful it all is," Huda said as she locked her car. "Come, let me show you around ... You see that splendid villa? It belongs to the Greek family that sold Baba the land on which *we* built our house."

I took note of the *we* bit; Huda had not yet been born then.

I did not want to dishearten her by pointing out that it was getting late and all that interested me, at that point, was to see the much-talked about villa of the Imam family. Needless to say, I was already emotionally drained from all we had experienced that afternoon. By now I knew perfectly well why I rarely venture outside the safety of my home in Ramallah.

"Here it is," Huda announced, pointing to a three-floor villa across the street from where we were standing. She had cleverly chosen the very best angle from which to appreciate the splendour of her family house.

"Wow," I said, "now I understand why you have been so fixated on your home. It is truly beautiful. Here, let me take a photo of you and your famous family house."

"*Yalla* Suad, go ahead and do it *quickly*; Nahil, come closer." Huda put her arm around Nahil, acting like the older cousin and then added, smiling at the thought, "I'm sure the family will love to see the two cousins posing in front of *the house.*"

I was taking my time, trying to position them in the lower corner of the frame. I must admit I was more interested in the architecture of the house than in the two cousins and family nostalgia. Unlike Nahil's house, Huda's was in an immaculate state.

"Now I see what you mean by the biggest real estate robbery."

"*Yalla* Suad, *khalsina,* get it over with, take the bloody photo before we get into trouble."

87

"Trouble!?!" I put down the camera.

"Why get into trouble?" Nahil asked, moving away from Huda.

"Oh well, I didn't want to alarm you, but now that Suad has seen the house and can write about it, I can tell you that I've been given a warning and threatened with deportation if I am ever caught or seen in the vicinity of our house again.

"In the past, whenever one of the Blumberg family living in our house, especially Yo'av, saw me in the garden or around the house, they would all come out screaming and yelling at me. It all started in 1997, when Udi Kaplan, the developer, bought our house from Amidar. Soon after he divided it into two apartments, one on each floor, then added the monster I told you about on top.

"During the two-year period of renovation, I often passed by to check on the work. And whenever circumstances allowed, I would pick up an un-mounted window, a door, a piece of railing. You've seen them in my Sheikh Jarrah house, Suad."

While Huda carried on dismantling her family house, I could not help feeling uncomfortable about her violating one of the cardinal principles of conservation: "Architectural details lose their historic significance once removed from their cultural context," I said.

Exactly like the Palestinians who lost their significance once they were removed from their natural habitat, their homeland, I thought to myself.

Huda was still at it: "One day I entered our house and found the Israeli family that had just bought the ground floor of our villa from Kaplan. I had the satisfaction of telling them *this was my family house*. Meanwhile I started loading some of the floor tiles that the contractor had put aside to reuse into the trunk of my car.

"I could see that with the first load of tiles they were too stunned to react, but in the few minutes it took me to return for the second load they regained their sense of ownership and tried to stop me. All I remember was that Mrs. Blumberg and I started screaming at one another, then shoving each other until we found ourselves on the floor. Her son, Yo'av, then ten or eleven years old, helped her up, while I was encouraged by the appearance of a sympathetic group of rabbis who had descended on me, no not from high heaven, but from the synagogue next door! Et voilà, since that day the house-war between the Blumberg family and me has never ceased."

Nahil and I stood there listening attentively. Meanwhile I wondered what had happened to hurrying before we "get into trouble". Huda was taking her time telling us her epic saga.

"Now, whenever Yo'av spots me or my car he calls the police, then blocks my way with his father's car until they arrive. So now I've learned to park far away so that I can run before the police arrive. Yo'av has become more efficient at it: he calls the police before he comes out to fight with me. As you see, with so much practice, we've both improved our war tactics."

Both! Perhaps she spoke too soon.

Only when Huda spotted the police van from a distance did I understand what she meant by the Blumbergs becoming much more efficient.

"Oh, my God! *Suad*, run, slither away like a snake before the police discover that you sneaked into Jerusalem with no permit; the rest I can handle perfectly on my own, I'm used to it by now."

With this out-of-the-blue sentence full of slithering, sneaking and snaking I was stunned for a few seconds, but got my act together and swiftly turned away, instinctively and instantly taking a left and disappearing down a side alley. However, running for my life did not stop me from caring about the frail seventy-eight-year-old Nahil.

"What about Nahil?" I asked as I was leaving.

"Nahil has a permit, she's legal. Suad, for God's sake, just dissolve!"

I walked fast, then speeded up, jogged and finally ran for all I was worth. Once I was at a safe distance I looked back; no one was coming after me. I sighed with relief and slowed down, allowing my heartbeat and adrenalin levels to stabilise. Huda's high-pitched voice, the angry tone of the police and the Blumbergs' screams all mingled with my late mother's voice: "Susu, habibti, escape is two-thirds of bravery, *il haribeh tultain il marajel.*"

Still, I could not help feeling guilty and sad that I had missed out on the central scene of my book: when the police arrested Huda, handcuffed her and pushed her into the back of their van.

While frail Nahil accompanied Huda to prison I ran all the way to Ramallah.

6

Mother and Child

Jerusalem 1942

It was love and an unbreakable bond between a mother and a child.

Her name was Aysheh
His name was Farid
She was born in 1891
He was born in 1909
She and everyone around her was ecstatic it was a boy
Soon after, she gave birth to three more
Fuad, Ni'mati, a little girl in a shadow, and baby Jamal who
    was in his mother's womb when his father died
Hence he carried his name: Jamal
Nevertheless
Aysheh's first love was called Farid
Her second love was called Farid
And her third and fourth loves were Farid and Farid
Her last and only love was Farid
Farid, Farid and only Farid
Farid in Arabic literally means: rare, unique, nothing like him,
    the only one
"Not Aysheh but Umm Farid" she'd rather be called
Mother of Farid

In 1930, Aysheh's husband Jamaleddine al-Imam died

She was then thirty-nine

And her beloved Farid was twenty-one

Together they cried as they placed the myrtle branches on
his grave in the Jerusalem Mamilla Cemetery

She sat there sobbing refusing to move

Not because she loved him dearly

But because she resented going back without him to her in-
laws

To the damp dark and crowded house in Bab al-Silsleh in the
Old City of Jerusalem

He helped his mother up, hugged her tightly, and made a
vow:

Mother, whatever it takes, you shall soon be back where you
belong.

To the posh neighbourhoods outside the city walls

To a splendour similar to that of her own family: the Aweidah
Compound

Back to the German Colony where she, Aysheh Aweidah, a
young and beautiful girl had blossomed

It took some time for him to realise his vow. Twelve years later,
in 1942, leaving everyone behind within the city walls, Farid
and his mother moved into their dream house in the lush green
neighbourhood of the Greek Colony. And as promised, just up
the road from the much talked about Aweidah Compound. They
proudly moved into their lovely new villa, roamed from one
grand room to another, from one spacious salon to another, from
one sunny balcony to the next. They climbed up and down the
oval stairs of their two-storey villa with Asmahan's voice in the
background: "*Balashh tibousni fi 'enayyah* ... Do not kiss me in
the eye, for a kiss in the eye ends in separation." Day and night,
rain or shine, Aysheh and Farid showed off their beautiful house,

receiving family members and entertaining friends, inviting all to long and detailed house and garden tours.

Aysheh and Farid lived there happily
But not for ever after

Like everyone around them, on May 20, 1948, under fire, bombardment and siege they had to rush out, leaving one of their ménage à trois behind.

They were never to set foot in their dream house again.

7

Husband and Wife (1958)

Sheikh Jarrah neighbourhood, in what had become East Jerusalem[9]

It was a tormented relationship between husband and wife
An older man and a much younger woman
Convenient for him and his mother, prestigious for her
At the end it was neither

A marriage that never bonded
But nevertheless it was fruitful
Five kids, five aitches: Hani, Hania, Huda, Hadi and Haitham

Her name was Bakiza
His name was Farid
And by now we know
He was born in 1909
She was born in 1939
When they married

---

[9] The city was called by its name Jerusalem. However in 1947 when the UN Security Council approved the creation of the state of Israel, Jerusalem was given a corpus-separatum status. As a result of the 1948 partition, the city was divided into West and East. Hence the new expressions, West and East, Jewish and Arab Jerusalem.

She was eighteen
He had just turned forty-eight.

Yet another forty-eight.
The insecurities that numbers gave him were countless
Hence he married the young and the beautiful

On their wedding day everyone pretended to be happy
Even Mama Aysheh danced that day
And meanwhile another house was being built – in East
   Jerusalem this time
The three of them: Aysheh, Farid and Bakiza moved in
   together
Ages: 70-48-18

The dynamics between the three should be left to the
imagination, and the wilder the imagination, the closer to reality.
Perhaps the archetype of mother and daughter-in-law was born
in Jerusalem. Bakiza was also crucified there.

8

Jealousy was only to be Expected
June 1967

Like all wars, each side thought they would win
One out of might and fear
And one out of naïvety and righteousness

Like many around them, Aysheh and Farid thought that the nineteen-year separation (1948-1967) from their dream house would soon come to an end: they would go back to the splendour of their neighbourhood and visit their many cherished places.

Meanwhile in their Sheikh Jarrah home in East Jerusalem it was business as usual – nothing out of the ordinary. Farid was in and out of his travel agency, busy cancelling reservations but also guiding the few optimistic tourists that remained around the Holy Land sites.

Teta Aysheh, also as usual, was bossing everyone around. She primarily bossed her daughter-in-law Bakiza, and then in descending order her five grandchildren: Hani, Hania, Huda, Hadi and even the little toddler Haitham, respectively thirteen, twelve, eight, seven and three years old.

"How could a mother with a family of five kids venture out of the house once, and often twice, a day? And only God knows where to!!" Teta Aysheh repeated a variation of this sentence once, and often twice, every single day. If words ceased to have an effect then desperate measures would follow: "Here, why don't you scrub the floor?" Teta Aysheh would shout, throwing a bucket full of water and soap on the living room floor or, to delay Bakiza even longer, on the rough stone tiles of the huge terrace.

So as not to get into trouble with her ageing and increasingly jealous husband, elegantly dressed and fully made-up Bakiza, though boiling on the inside, obeyed. Such jealousy and vindictive acts often delayed her outings but never prevented them. Still elegantly dressed, she would quickly mop up the water and swiftly run out of the door, down the stairs and out of the gate before Teta Aysheh could think of another household chore.

In a conventional and narrow-minded town like Jerusalem, rumours and gossip were not favourable regarding young and beautiful Bakiza. With an often absent husband and a strict and increasingly jealous mother-in-law, Bakiza was always leaving the house in search of small adventures here and there before going back to a large and demanding family.

Just a day before the war started, and in anticipation of heavy fighting in their Sheikh Jarrah neighbourhood, all the children were to go and stay with their other Teta, Bakiza's mother, who lived a few kilometers north of Jerusalem in the town of Beit Hanina. Well-equipped with argumentative skills and stubbornness, Huda managed to get the three elders, Mama, Baba, and Teta, to succumb to her wish to stay home with them.

That evening, like most summer evenings, Teta Aysheh sat on the big terrace overlooking the Nablus Road. While the main street was buzzing nervously below, the five kids' usual skirmishes were reduced to Huda's solitary hyperactivity. It seemed that both Teta and Huda were missing the four children.

While Bakiza was running between the kitchen and the balcony preparing a late summer dinner, Huda ran excitedly in and out displaying her new clothes, the white dress and matching shoes which Mama had bought her for Eid al-Adha, the approaching Feast of the Sacrifice.

While Huda was trying to see her reflection in the shiny white Clarks shoes, she called out piercingly to her grandmother, "Teta …Teta … Teta … See how shiny my new shoes are!" She then placed them on the table in front of her Teta.

"Never place shoes on dining tables!"

"But they're new, Teta!"

"I know they're new, but *a shoe is a shoe.*"

Huda instantly picked them up, hugging them close to her chest and looking at them lovingly. "I'll go and put on my white and pink Eid dress and the matching socks and shoes."

"For God's sake, Huda, *no*, not now!" Teta and Mama scolded simultaneously.

Perhaps this was the very first time that Huda was not in a position to manipulate her mother's and grandmother's conflicting opinions. More often than not she exploited their differences to do what *she* liked.

"Let us hope there will be two feasts soon: Eid al-Adha and the greater Eid of returning to our house in the Greek Colony in West Jerusalem." Teta Aysheh stared fixedly for a few seconds and then fell to prayer: "Ya Rab, ya Rab, ya Rab, please, please, please God." It was one of those rare times when Huda heard or saw Teta reciting suras from the Quran. Teta was so strong, she never needed God. Once done with her recitation, she happily announced, "Soon you will see how beautiful our house in West Jerusalem is …"

Huda interrupted her, "Yes, yes, Teta, I know, I know it by heart. 'Nothing compares to the house Farid and I built next to my parents' compound: the Aweidah Compound.'" Huda mimicked her grandmother's words in a chanting tone and giggled.

Aysheh's four grandchildren often repeated her exact words, giggling at the same time. They'd heard their grandmother speak those words hundreds of times until they were sick and tired. Even three-year old Haitham was starting to imitate Teta's refrain.

Like the other kids, Huda made fun of Teta's romantic memories of her house, but she harboured a secret: the only reason that made her stay behind with the adults was that she would be the very first one among the siblings to see *The House*. She so much wanted to see the one thing that made her Baba sad, so sad that it even made him cry.

Having given up the idea of putting on her Eid costume Huda quietly settled down next to Aysheh. They were both waiting for Farid to appear with the latest war news, and for Bakiza to bring out the very yummy cool summer dishes: yogurt with cucumbers, garlic, and mint, white goat cheese, her delicious tabuleh, the crunchy breaded fattouch salad, sliced tomatoes, sliced cucumbers, green and black olives, and lemon squash with mint and crushed ice – everything that quenches the thirst of a hot June evening.

As expected, Farid came late that night. "It seems that both armies, the Jordanian and the Israeli, are ready for war. This evening Jordanian tanks were seen moving close to the Mandelbaum Gate."

"Farid! You and I can go and live in our house in the Greek Colony again," Teta said, smiling.

"Teta! I thought you were taking me to see the house! Are you leaving Mama and me behind? Are you and Baba going to live there alone?" There was nervous laughter in response to Huda's not-so-innocent remark.

"*Wilik*, you naughty little thing. Not a bad idea, though. My son and I go back to live in our house in the Greek Colony while you and your mother stay in this house. A fair division, I

99

would say." Teta leaned forward and tickled little Huda under her chin.

"Not a bad idea. I like that," Bakiza replied, trying to take control of an uncertain world around her.

Feeling a bit nervous about the direction in which the conversation was heading Farid lovingly interfered, addressing his wife this time: "No, seriously, Bakiza, which house would you rather live in?"

It was one of the very few times that Farid had hugged his wife so passionately in front of his mother and little daughter. He sighed as he let go of her. "Soon we'll all be able to go to West Jerusalem to see our Greek Colony house. I wonder what has become of it. I wonder if the furniture is still there, if the garden is in good shape. I wonder who lives in it now. Is it possible that it was left empty all these years? Nineteen years is a long time. They've felt like nineteen decades."

"Soon we'll find out ... Ya Rab!" said his mother.

Once again little Huda rejoiced in her father's beaming smile and the sparkle that appeared in his eyes whenever his house was mentioned.

This time there was real hope
Hope that they would be able to return to their house in
    West Jerusalem
Hope for Bakiza, but also for her mother-in-law
Each to finally be in her own kingdom!

9

Photo Albums
June 7, 1967

The rumours were right.

The war did indeed break out on the morning of June 5th.

Israeli tanks conquered East Jerusalem in no time.

And Israeli soldiers were entering Palestinian homes in less time.

It was not clear which was faster, the banging of the Israeli soldiers on the front door, or the consumption of the celebrities' photographs by the orange flames.

Farid stood in front of the fireplace and fed the flickering flames fragments of his past. No one understood, not even Farid himself, what was going on in his head to make him burn the photographs of all the important personages in his life. Having been an official guide for the Jordanian Royal Palace, he had many such photos.

His mother Aysheh stood next to him nervously, imploring, "But why? Tell me why? Weren't you the one who always said, 'If, and only if, I could have saved my photo albums? They [the Israelis] not only stole my dream house but also my photo albums. A man with no photos is a man with no memories, with no childhood, it always felt as if I was born at the age of thirty-eight.' For God's sake Farid, stop this foolishness. They are not here to look at your photo albums." She was trembling.

101

But Aysheh also understood her son's fears: Farid did not want to be associated with King Hussein of Jordan. He was terrified of being interrogated.

Her entreaties were in vain. One photo after the other, Farid's recent past was disappearing.

Celebrities' Photographs

Here he was with a beaming face posing next to His Majesty King Hussein.

Here was Farid standing next to Her Majesty Queen Dina, the king's first cousin and also his first wife. These photos must have been taken sometime in the early Fifties. Here he was standing tall next to Emperor Haile Selassie of Ethiopia. Compared to the emperor, Farid looked like a giant.

When it came to burning the photos of the gorgeous Queen Farah Diba (the second wife of the Shah of Iran, Ali Mohammad Pahlavi) both Farid and the flames trembled, but sadly her beauty was also consumed.

Farid stared at his photo with President Habib Bourgouiba of Tunisia who had visited Jerusalem just a few weeks earlier. During that visit Bourgouiba had made his inflammatory statement: "Israel should be recognised by all the Arab countries." Even though this controversial remark had made headlines and sparked demonstrations across the Arab world, the photograph could be of great use today. Farid's shaking hands carefully placed Bourgouiba's photo in the centre of the coffee table behind him.

While Zohrab was King Hussein's private photographer, Farid was the official guide to all His Majesty's celebrity guests, including Pope John Paul V, who was about to enter the fiery flames when Bakiza took Farid by the arm, begging him to stop. "For God's sake, Farid, stop it, don't burn the Pope, it'll bring us bad luck."

Being married into a prominent Muslim family in Jerusalem,

102

the Imams, Aysheh was not exactly amused at the idea of being protected by the Pope. Nevertheless, she also thought that burning his image would bring misfortune to the household.

At this point a shaken Huda intervened by running to her father, tugging at the tails of his white shirt and repeating her mother's words, "Please, Baba, open the door before the crazy Israeli soldiers blow it apart."

Eventually Farid submitted to his daughter's demands and also sought the Pope's blessings, placing his photo next to those of President Bourgouiba, and heading for the door to open it for the screaming soldiers:

"*Iftakh, iftakh!*" BANG ... BANG "*Iftakh il bab!*"

"Stay put, keep still, do not move from the living room," shouted their commander as the other three soldiers began searching every corner of the house: up to the roof, into the attic, the bedrooms, under the beds, in the cupboards, behind the curtains, into Farid's study, out onto the balcony, and soon into the kitchen.

Not finding the phantoms they feared, the soldiers relaxed a little. One picked up an apple and started munching on it. He seemed to be hungry. If they start the war as early as three o'clock in the morning it is not surprising that by noon they would all be hungry.

So as not to make the Israeli army look undisciplined and feeble, the same soldier while still munching on his apple gave his orders in a commanding, sweet-apple voice, using his rifle to point at each one of them. "All of you, get ready to leave the house: you, you, you and you."

The soldier's last *you* landed on grandmother Aysheh. He had no idea of the trouble he had just got himself into. "You, you, you, and *YOU!*" Teta Aysheh yelled back at the soldier, stretching her right arm full-length as well as her index finger to point at each soldier in turn. With so much anger, grandmother's extended arm looked much more threatening than the soldiers' machine guns. Nevertheless, her facial expressions were so comical that she succeeded in uniting the enemies in nervous laughter.

In the tirade that followed she voiced her *arghs*, mocking the young soldier, rolling her tongue and twisting her thick lips.

She relished her role as the unafraid elderly woman. "*Ya wlad il* ... sons of ..." but stopped herself from saying bitches or calling them bastards. "Listen, you boys. In 1948 you took my house in the Greek Colony and my parents' house in Upper Baq'a and now, nineteen years later, you come again telling us to leave our house in East Jerusalem! Why don't *you* go back to wherever you came from! Go back to Russia, to Poland, to New York, Hungary or wherever. For God's sake, just leave us alone!" Her voice broke at this point. Looking at Farid for assurance she added, "We are not leaving."

Then, just in case, she corrected herself: "I am not leaving my house, do you hear me, little mouse? Do you have any idea how old I am? I am *eighty* years old. Do you hear me? Eight-zero. I am older than your grandmother. I shall not leave my house ever again, and will not allow you to take it, no, not over my dead body. Never!"

She then curled up on the pink sofa and wept.

Her daughter-in-law took note of the three extra years Teta Aysheh had added to her age. Until the very last day of Teta's life Bakiza kept teasing her, "It took an Israeli army commander to make you admit your *real* age."

"Get ready to leave," the commanding officer repeated his firm orders. Coming closer to the pink sofa where Farid stood tall to protect his mother, he addressed him man-to-man and face-to-face this time. "She can stay behind if she wants, but the three of you have to come down with me. Follow me."

"Down where?" inquired Farid. He did not know what to make of the commander's order. Did it mean that they would return home soon? But what if they didn't? Isn't that what happened in 1948? He recalled all the horror stories of people leaving an elderly person or a child behind, thinking they would be back in an hour or so. One story after another echoed in Farid's ears. The images of the 1948 Nakba in which tens of thousands of Palestinians were forced out of their homes were still vivid in his mind. It felt as if it had all happened yesterday. But wasn't 1948 only yesterday?

"No way, I will not leave my house," Teta repeated adamantly. And when Teta Aysheh said something more than once everyone in her family understood. It was final. Teta would stay behind.

Farid also knew that, as with his mother Aysheh, when an Israeli army commander gave a military order, that too was final.

Huda rushed to her bedroom mumbling: I will never leave ... I will never leave.

Get ready to leave the house ... Get ready to leave the house.

She believed it was the end. Having heard, over and over again, the stories told and retold by her Baba and Teta Aysheh about their last hours in the Greek Colony house, and also about what had happened to the little boys and girls in the nearby village of Deir Yasin[10], Huda knew that they were all going to die. But one thing was for sure: she was not going to leave her shining new white Clarks shoes behind, nor the matching pink and white dress.

She would go in style.

How appropriate for Eid al-Adha, the feast of sacrifice, she thought. Her schoolteacher had explained the story behind this

---

[10] Deir Yasin was an Arab village located next to Jerusalem. In 1948 the Jewish forces massacred the majority of its inhabitants. Many believed that as a result of this massacre many Palestinians got scared and ran away from the neighbouring villages.

feast: it celebrated the time when the Prophet Ibrahim was going to sacrifice his son Ishmael.

From that day on, Huda had been ready to be sacrificed in style.

Just before leaving her room, after a final check in the mirror, her eyes fell on the photos of her three brothers and sister: Hani, Hania, Hadi and cute little Haitham. Only then did she realise how much she had missed them. Only then did she realise how lucky they were not to be dragged out into the street to meet their end.

She was reaching for the framed pictures when she heard her mother's anxious call. "Huda! Huda! Where are you?"

"Coming!" Composed, she called back. But that did not stop her from climbing onto a chair and reaching the high shelf where the photo frames stood. She held each of them close to her face, stared at them for a while, hugged them close to her chest, before giving them long and loud kisses: mua, mua, mua, mua, one by one.

Did Huda cry?

No.

"Bye Hania, bye Hani, bye Hadi and bye habibi Haitham." She put the framed photos back and waved her little hand.

"Huda habibti, why did you put on your Eid clothes?" her mother asked, standing in the doorway.

"I want to die in my best clothes."

"Oh, habibti, no one is going to die." Bakiza hugged little Huda tightly and wept. Even the soldiers standing there realised that Bakiza's tears and sorrow had nothing to do with having to leave her mother-in-law behind.

The four Israeli soldiers escorted Farid, Bakiza and Huda down the staircase into the garden, and then out onto Nablus Road.

She looked around her and saw hordes of people gathered in the street: men, women, children, the very old, the very young, and every age in between. Still preoccupied with her make-believe death-squad scenario, Huda was surprised that no one seemed to be properly dressed for the occasion. Some were even in their pajamas.

Her heart skipped a beat when she saw a very deep and extremely long and undulating ditch in the middle of the wide sidewalk where she and her street mates usually played hopscotch. She wondered what all these people were doing in this tightly packed ditch that made her think of a long sardine tin.

She wondered when the Israelis had had time to do the digging. They must have dug it during the first hours of the war when they were all hiding under the dining table. She had been unable to hear the noise of the digging in the midst of so much shooting, bombing, and the screeching of fighter planes flying over their heads.

When and where did the Israeli soldiers find such a huge number of Arab men, women and children? All of them, like naughty school children, had their hands held over their heads. This must be the death ditch, she thought. It all made sense now.

Some were silent
Some were weeping
Some were moaning
Some were asked to speak up
Some were asked to shut the fuck up
Some were scared
Some were resigned
Some were told to sit
Some were told to stand
Some like Huda believed they were about to face their God.

Meanwhile, the four soldiers escorted Huda and her parents

here, led them there, walked them up the road next to the deep ditch, walked them back along the same sidewalk and then alongside the long death ditch. The ditch was packed, there was not a single space left to fill.

So much for Israeli military planning and their miscalculation regarding the number of Jerusalemite Arab residents whose land they had just occupied. They got rid of the Arabs in West Jerusalem only to find them once again in East Jerusalem.

Tired of their heavy human burden the Israeli soldiers released Farid, Bakiza and Huda.

"Just go back home," yelled the same Israeli commander with the same self-confidence all military people pretend to have.

Huda could not believe her luck, not only did her Eid outfit survive, but her parents had survived as well. Released, the three of them ran back home like bullets to Teta and the safety of their own home. As they were about to disappear behind the door, one of the soldiers fired a stream of bullets in their direction. The glass windows of the front veranda shattered.

"It is because of those unexpected bullets and unjustified aggressive behaviour that I never trusted the Israelis ever again," Huda confessed to me forty-four years later, as she and I drank tea in the same house, in the same living room, and on the same pink sofa where Teta had sat, anxiously waiting for them to return.

10

The Visit
three weeks after the 1967 War

Baba always kept a promise
But this time he did not
Every time I asked him, why not? he replied:
Whenever Teta Aysheh is ready we shall go
And when I repeatedly begged Teta to get ready she said:
Whenever Farid is ready we shall go
For weeks I was a pendulum between the two
And when I probed Mama to intervene she said indifferently:
Whenever Farid and Mama Aysheh are ready we shall go.

Whenever Baba was smartly dressed I would say:
"Now that you're ready why don't we go?"

And whenever Teta was elegantly dressed I would beg her:
"Teta, didn't you always promise to take me to your house the
minute they open East to West?"

Teta often kept quiet, then sighed and moaned, "*Akhhh, ya
Teta, akhhh ...*"

This went on for weeks.
Until Uncle Hassan, Baba's best friend, showed up early one
afternoon to declaim, "Yalla, come on everyone, get ready, we
are going to visit your house in West Jerusalem."

Wow, at last! I was in seventh heaven. I jumped up and clapped my hands and ran around the living room twice before disappearing into my bedroom. I slipped into my Eid al-Adha clothes and in no time was all dressed up in my pink and white dress and my Clarks shoes, excited and ready to go.

But when I stepped into the living room, *Oh God!* Teta and Baba were not yet ready: they were sitting on the pink sofa staring at one another. Uncle Hassan was sitting on the edge of his seat opposite them. "Listen to me, Farid, listen to me, Aunt Aysheh: you will never ever be psychologically ready for this visit."

It was the very first time I had heard the expression "*psychologically ready*". However, I have put it to great use and abuse ever since.

Teta and Baba gazed into each other's eyes for a long, long time.

Then when Baba looked away, Teta cried.

And I intervened: "Teta, didn't you always say it will be the *biggest* Eid feast when we go back to our house in West Jerusalem? So why are you crying?"

Little did I understand.

We were not going back to live in our dream house in West Jerusalem, we were only going to visit it.

And how does one visit one's own house?

I did not understand then.

And I do not understand now.

It did not make sense to me then.

And it does not make sense to me now.

And ever since that first visit, nothing around me made sense again.

From East to West

It was Teta who insisted we walk to our house; the distance

110

between our two houses was a thirty-or forty-minute walk, she claimed.

So when Uncle Hassan suggested we go by car, Teta vehemently objected: "Do you have any idea what has become of West Jerusalem in the last nineteen years? It would be much safer if we went on foot." Baba seemed convinced. Uncle Hassan realised it was not the right moment to argue with a nervous wreck like Teta. I had no clue why a happy occasion like this was causing so much tension. A long-held dream was about to be fulfilled, why so much fear and apprehension?

Once the difficult decisions were made everyone felt energised.

Soon we were all trotting in disorderly rows on the narrow sidewalk.

Teta and Baba in the first row with Uncle Hassan.

Hani and Hania, whose teenage energy made them flit back and forth, left, right and centre, were also ahead of us.

While my little brother Hadi and I were hostages to Mama's tight fists.

I was eight. Hadi was seven.

I later thanked God that our three-year-old toddler, Haitham, was left behind.

The trip between our two houses took many turns and as many ups and downs. Down the hill from Sheikh Jarrah, up the road to the Musrara neighbourhood and then through an empty space full of debris, rubble, broken fences and barbed wire. That was when the first words were uttered: "We have just entered West Jerusalem," Baba's trembling voice announced.

We fell back into silence.

For one reason or another Baba's announcement made me joyful, very joyful: at last we are in West Jerusalem, the paradise that Teta, Baba and everyone around me had gone on about for as long as I could remember.

"Nothing is as beautiful as West Jerusalem."

"Nothing is as splendid as our house in the lush green neighbourhood of the Greek Colony."

"Nothing is as stunning as 1948 Palestine."

And finally I was in the "lost paradise".

I was trying to absorb everything around me: houses with red-tiled roofs, apartment buildings, tall cypress and pine trees, cars, signs in a language I did not comprehend, white and blue flags on top of buildings, small shops, and the Yahud (Jews). As much as my parents and their friends talked about the Yahud, I had never seen one before. The first Israelis I saw were the four soldiers who came to our house three weeks ago: exactly on June 7. And they were horrible.

I tightened my hold on Mama's fist.

I stared at every person that passed by: some were dark, some were brown, some were fair and some were as blond as Aunty Liz from London. The thing that drew my attention the most was the teenage boys and girls who were the same age as Hani and Hania. Unlike us they were shabbily dressed: they all wore shorts, T-shirts and sandals. I had no idea why, but for days on end all Hani and Hania talked about were the Israeli sandals.

Everything seemed under control until we entered an old "black and white" neighbourhood. It felt like all those old films I never liked, except for the Charlie Chaplin ones that made me laugh. But this film frightened me; it made me tremble from the inside. I pushed against Mama's warm body, my two hands clutching her arm tightly. "Stop it, habibti Huda, there is nothing to be scared of. These are normal people like you and I," but her tone was neither convinced nor convincing.

"But Mama, why is everyone and everything in this *hara* (neighbourhood) in black and white? Can't someone do a colour tint for them, frame by frame, as you once explained they did with old black and white films?" Mama's giggles relaxed me a little, but not enough.

112

Looking at the black and white people made me sweat. Though it was late June, huge men were dressed in winter clothes. Some even wore big round fur hats. I thought my eyes were playing tricks on me, like when I stare at the sun. Everything around me was black, black and more black; long black frocks, coats, black shoes, black knee-socks, black shorts or trousers, black hats, long black beards, black hair shaved around the neck, long black side locks, and black cords dangling from both sides of their waists. I had no idea what these were for and didn't dare ask. The only thing that was not black was the long-sleeved white shirts.

Even boys my age wore black suits, black hats and long-sleeved white shirts.

Old and young women alike wore black. Not attractive black dresses; long black skirts, thick black stockings, black shawls and black head coverings, scarves and strange hair. And since the only time I had seen Teta, Mama and my three aunts wear completely black outfits was when Uncle Adel died, I asked, "Mama, whom are they mourning?"

"No one," Mama replied dismissively.

A little way ahead I saw four boys my age. They came running from a narrow side alley. They were the exact opposite, the negative, of the boys in black. They had light beige knee-length coats, same length robes, white belts wrapped around the open coats, white knee-socks and white conical hats. Everything they wore was beige or white, except for the black shoes. They too had their blond hair shaved around the neck with long blond side curls.

Unlike everything that Teta and Baba had told us all these years, West Jerusalem was very shabby and poor. There were clotheslines with black and white laundry strung across the streets as well as over the public squares. Unlike our big and beautiful Sheikh Jarrah pink stone houses, those in this black and white neighbourhood were small, untidy and built of dirty grey concrete. I was so perplexed that I asked, "Mama, is this a Palestinian refugee camp?"

"No."

With such a definite no for an answer I had to figure out things all by myself. I kept dragging my feet in the narrow, unattractive and crowded streets of West Jerusalem. Oh, how much I wished that Teta and Baba would give up the idea of going back to our house in the West. I so wanted to return to our safe street and to our lovely house and garden in our beautiful East Jerusalem.

I also had no idea why these black and white people had put up so many huge black and white newspapers on their walls. I had never seen such large newspapers in such strange letters. Even Baba couldn't read them. Finally we came to a big sign which had one sentence in big red English letters. I was so delighted to finally see some colour and familiar letters, which my brother Hani read out loud: "PLEASE DO NOT PASS THROUGH OUR NEIGHBOURHOOD IN IMMODEST CLOTHES."

I automatically pulled down my pink and white dress – just in case.

All the men who stood next to the bulletin boards reading those enormous posters were wearing eyeglasses with thick lenses. I noticed that even little boys and girls in this area wore thick eyeglasses.

At that point, I recalled (but kept to myself) what our schoolteacher, Miss Leila, had once explained, "Boys and girls who play with themselves end up wearing thick eyeglasses." I still remember how we cracked up laughing at poor Salma, our classmate with thick eyeglasses, and how much Salma cried that day. All I remember was that next day both Miss Leila and Salma disappeared from our school forever.

It wasn't until much later that I realised we were in the Jewish neighbourhood of Mea She'arim, where all the Orthodox Haredim lived.

Once out of that neighbourhood there was colour everywhere in West Jerusalem. With the colourful background Teta and Baba became animated.

Everything was familiar to them; I could hardly keep up or remember who lived where, whose office that was, and who owned what. They were pointing here, there and everywhere:

"Here's Jaffa Street; here is where we did our shopping."

"Look, look, look! Here's the post office building. See those two beautiful buildings over there? One belonged to my father and the other belonged to Uncle Adel."

"Here is Cinema Edison, this is where Umm Kulthum and Asmahan sang."

"Look over there, that's the tower of the YMCA where I used to swim."

"Opposite is the famous King David Hotel, we'll pass by them soon."

Unlike the black and white Mea She'arim quarter, everything around us was nice and pretty.

Ya Allah, shoo hilweh inti ya falasteen. Oh God, Palestine, you are so beautiful!

I kept the thought to myself.

Everything was delightful and fun until we got to Mamilla Cemetery. Ah, I suddenly remembered, this is where Jiddo Grandpa Jamal is buried. The minute we walked into the cemetery Teta took the lead. She seemed so familiar with all those scary graves. Both Teta and Baba knew everyone's name and everybody's family in this rundown cemetery:

"Here is Ibrahim Hindiyeh, *Alla yerhamu*, may God have mercy on his soul."

"Here is Said Dajani, *Alla yerhamu*, may God have mercy on his soul."

115

"Here is his wife, Nahid Dajani, *Alla yerhamha*, may God have mercy on her soul."

"Here is Abu Khaled Nashashibi, *Allah yerhamu*, may God have mercy on his soul."

"Here is Siham Husseini, *Alla yerhamha*, may God have mercy on her soul."

There were so many dead people in this cemetery it felt as if Teta and Baba had left behind more dead relatives and friends than were still alive.

Teta seemed to be composed till we got to Grandpa's grave. Her words were soon drowned by sobs. "Jamal, I am so sorry we left you all alone for so long." She knelt down on Jiddo's dusty grave and wept loudly. Soon we were all crying in various degrees. Once done reading al Fatiha, Baba leaned against his Mama, hugging her tightly.

They seemed to be in a world of their own.

11

A Dream House

Oh God, Teta was absolutely right.

Oh God, Baba was also absolutely right.

Oh God, our house in West Jerusalem is absolutely gorgeous.

And every single thing that Teta had told us over all those years was also true. Our house in West Jerusalem was by far more beautiful than the one in East Jerusalem. The eight of us huddled close to one another. We seemed to be strangers in familiar surroundings.

We stood at an angle on the sidewalk across the street from our house. "Stand still and don't move!" Baba nervously instructed Hani and Hania who were too excited to keep still. Like all of us, they so much wanted to cross the street and enter our house which stood in the midst of a lush green garden.

Like Baba and Teta, we all stood across the street and stared at the house. We stood still, so awestruck, it felt as if we were visiting a holy shrine.

"See how beautiful," Baba eventually spoke. He was addressing Mama this time.

"Gorgeous," replied Mama.

I could see Teta's eyes twinkling, I could see she wanted to say, "See Bakiza, I told you so." Instead she kept quiet, very quiet. Baba carried on, "See how beautiful the three-arch entrance is!

117

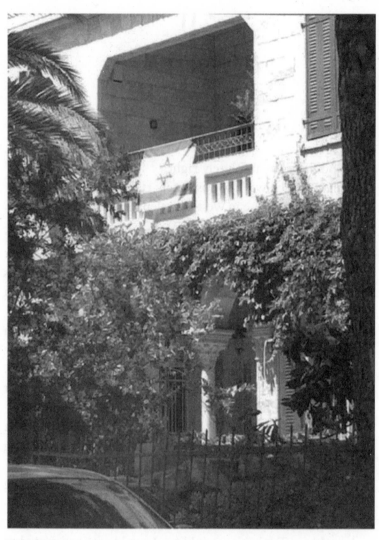

The Imam house in the Greek Colony, West Jerusalem.

Look how intricate the carvings are on the Corinthian capitals. It was on this veranda that Teta and I had our morning coffee every day." He gave Teta a warm hug.

I could hardly see the three stone arches Baba was talking about, partly because I was a tiny eight-year-old girl who did not want to ruin her shiny Clarks shoes by standing on her toes, and partly because the three arches and the carved thing were hidden behind the trees: the palm, the pomegranate and the lemon trees that Baba had talked about so much.

"And look how beautiful that stone balustrade on the second floor is. That was where we had dinner every summer evening." Like the Corinthian capitals, I had no clue what a stone balustrade was but kept quiet. Baba continued. "See the green shutters on the ground floor? That is where my study and library were. And you see the shutters upstairs? On the left was Teta's bedroom and on the right was mine. The big kitchen and veranda were on the other side, in the back. The big salon with the lovely colourful tiles was on the ground floor, the living room with the nice Persian carpets was on the first floor."

I was not sure why Baba was giving us all this explanation while we stood outside the house so I said, "Baba, let's go see the inside."

"Wait, habibti, wait, we have to see how they'll react."

Before I had a chance to ask Baba who "they" were and what he meant by "react" he was crossing the street, moving cautiously towards his house. Like an excited herd we all followed him: Hani, Hania, Teta, Uncle Hassan, Mama, Hadi and I.

The second, or even before Baba could take hold of the metal handle to open the cast-iron gate to the garden, a dog barked, and soon after a woman in a blue dress appeared at the front door, right behind the three stone arches that Baba had been talking about.

She took a few steps forward and stood at the top of the five steps that separated her balcony level from the lower garden level where Baba stood. "*Ken, toda raba*, yes, good day."

"*Toda raba*," Baba answered, then switched to English. "I am Farid al-Imam, the owner of this house, and I would like to show it to my wife and family, my mother who ..."

Before Baba could finish his sentence, all hell broke loose. There was shrieking and squeaking ... a rapid-fire barrage of Hebrew, Arabic and English words and short phrases.

"*Bagha! Bagha! Bagha! Leish inta houn? Bagha! Bagha!*" (Out! Out! Out! Why are you here?) What the hell are you doing here?" She switched from broken Arabic to broken English. "Get out of here right away before I call the police! Sara! Sara!" She yelled at the top of her voice for her teenage daughter who was by then standing right next to her.

"There's no need to call the police or make such a fuss, I simply want to show my wife and children our house," Baba said as he pointed to us. I could see his arm and body were shaking. Uncle Hassan stood right next to him.

"No! You cannot show anybody anything! I say go away or I will call the police!" She turned to her daughter, "Sara, Sara, call the police!" But the daughter remained frozen at her side.

Mother and daughter and the little dog resumed their screaming cacophony of broken Arabic, broken English, broken barking, broken Hebrew, then Polish (this I learnt from Baba later, though it also sounded broken to my ears).

Shouting back at the two women Uncle Hassan protested, "I don't understand why you are acting so hysterically, there is no need for all this." He put his arms around my frozen Baba as Mama and Teta pushed us back across the street.

The woman continued to scream. The daughter by her side also screamed. The frantic little dog stood right next to his master's feet and barked, he barked and barked, endlessly barked and barked, barked and snarled.

120

At that point we had no choice but to turn our backs and retreat down the hill.

For the whole of the forty-five minute walk back home all I could hear was the dog barking and the Jewish family growling.

And forty-five years later, I can still recall the little dog's hysterical barking.

Baba's rolling tears.

And Teta's unceasing sobs.

And it was on that day that I made a vow to keep visiting our house as long as I live, and as frequently as I can.

A constant reminder of *whose house it is.*

A vow that has since become an obsession.

An obsession that became as heavy as life itself.

12

The Prison
July 2011

Huda did not sleep that night
But she may have dozed off
And since this was her first night ever in prison
This was only to be expected

She slit open her right eye to look at her watch
It was missing
Only then did she recall what had happened to her the day
    before
She closed her eyes
And sighed

Dawn and breakfast arrived together.

She was keen on the first but could not be bothered with the
second. She could not tell which made her stomach turn more,
the stench of early morning eggs, or the exchange of Hebrew
and Arabic yelling between the prisoners and their wardens.
She did not know why there was such a commotion to get up
so early in the morning if one is to remain locked up the whole
long day, a few weeks, a few months, a few years or even a few
lifetimes, like her neighbour Sharif, who got a few life sentences
in prison.

This new perspective she had on Sharif's misfortune gave

her the shivers, and her heart sank as she turned on the thin damp sponge they called a mattress. Untypically (these were unusual circumstances after all), like her Teta she prayed to God: "Ya Rab, ya Rab, ya Rab, please God, release me from prison soon."

"Good morning, Huda. Inshallah, I hope you slept well last night."

Oh God, who is that? Ah, Samira! She remembered her cellmate. "My eyes never closed, not for one second," Huda complained, stretching out both arms.

"Not true, I heard you snore and talk in your sleep," Samira replied with a smile, leaning against the iron bars.

"Sleep-talk! You must be kidding! That can't be true." At first Huda tried to deny the accusation but then quickly gave in, she knew about her own sleep-talking already. "What did I say? Tell me, what did I say?" Huda felt awkward about a possible embarrassment; she squatted apprehensively on her mattress to await the truth.

"Who is Hani?" Samira asked, then started laughing.

"Hey, don't let your imagination run wild. Hani is my son, al-hamdulilah balash fadaieh, thank God, no scandals," Huda replied with a forced smile.

"You were also calling for or yelling at your mother," Samira added.

"Most likely yelling. Oh God, I thought I would get a break from Bakiza, my mother, at least for one night. It seems she accompanied me even to al-Maskoubiyyeh (the Russian Compound)."[11]

With a half-smile Samira added, "Habibti, let me tell you, mothers never leave us, not even after they're dead. My mother passed away a few years ago and she still appears in all my dreams.

---

[11] The Russian Compound is a police station, interrogation and detention centre in West Jerusalem.

She's always scolding me, 'Samira, I told you *not this way!*
Everything you do or say is *wrong, wrong, wrong!*' I sometimes
dream of her running after me with a raised slipper, trying to
smack me – I often wake up in a sweat because of her."

Oh my God! This woman must be well into her sixties and
her mother still smacks her! Mine is an angel by comparison,
Huda thought to herself.

It did not take long for Samira to forget her mother's flying
slipper and turn her attention to her early morning breakfast.
She peeled an egg, came up to Huda and offered it to her. "Here,
habibti, have this. You must be starving by now. You were so
angry when you arrived here last night that you didn't touch
your dinner. Here, eat this."

Huda clutched at her stomach and turned her head away.
She was about to throw up. "I can't. My stomach is turning,"
she managed to get the words out of compressed lips, then
swallowed her saliva.

"Okay."

In no time Samira's mouth was full of egg. She ate hers first,
then Huda's, one after the other, followed by a cracker. She was
now chewing away leisurely and rolling her tongue. The
offensive chomping wouldn't end …

Huda finally had enough. She not so subtly covered her face
with her hand to shield her nostrils against the smell. Once she
was done munching her eggs, Samira again tried to tempt Huda
into eating something. "Try this. I tell you, their jams are
delicious. Try this yummy apricot one. Believe me, these Jewish
jams are even better than the ones I make at home. Goddamn,
whatever they do, they do well, not like us Arabs."

Huda did not agree with her cellmate on Jewish supremacy
in jam-making, but she let it go. "No, Samira. Please leave me
alone, I can't eat anything." Huda stretched out on the mattress,
desperately turning her face to the wall.

"Okay, okay, I see you're still upset, my dear Huda. Soon you'll get used to prison. Remember, we're all here because of our love for our country, not because we've committed a crime against them. They commit all sorts of crimes against us, then turn around and arrest us and throw us into prison. Remember, habibti, one-third of Palestinian men have been to Israeli prisons – do you think they were all criminals?" She barely paused for breath before continuing. "Umm Sabri, the cleaning woman who was here before you, was arrested because she sneaked into Israel without a work permit. Poor thing, she was even older than me. Her two sons are in prison, and imagine, she has to work at her age to feed nine grandchildren."

Ignoring Huda's moans Samira carried on. "And the young woman, Siham, the one who left yesterday before you arrived, she was from Ramallah, from a village near Ramallah, I forget the name, it could've been Bibwan, Beitunia, Betinia, something that starts with a B. Anyway to cut a long story short, she came to visit her mother in the Al-Maqased Hospital[12] and she was arrested because she didn't have the necessary permit to visit Jerusalem. Siham was like you; she cried day and night for a week until someone from her family eventually bailed her out. I tell you, we're a money-making machine for the Israelis and that's all there is to it. 'Security' my ass."

Huda, whose headache was getting worse as a result of Samira's incessant stream of stories could not help but appreciate the "security my ass". "If the security of a country means the annihilation of another nation then there must be something structurally wrong with that country," she said in response.

Samira totally ignored Huda's intellectual remark and carried on recounting the stories of those who had passed through her

---

[12] Al-Maqased is the largest Arab hospital in East Jerusalem. No Palestinians living in the West Bank or Gaza Strip can reach it because they are not given permits to enter East Jerusalem.

prison cell. "The one before Siham was from the town of Anata. They arrested her because she tied herself to one of her olive trees when Jewish settlers tried to burn it. She was lucky not to have been burned along with her trees. Trust me, the settlers would do it. And the Silwani woman was imprisoned because she shoved the Israeli official who handed her the demolition order for her house. When the bulldozer arrived she refused to leave, so they carried her away and brought her to me."

Huda was getting tired and terribly bored with all these depressing yet familiar stories. She realised how eager Samira was to have a listening ear, having spent so many months in prison not knowing when the next cellmate might arrive. With difficulty Huda finally managed to interrupt her torrent of stories. "And you, Samira, how long have you been in prison to know about all these cases?"

"Four months. But this is my third time. And this time, excuse my language, Sitt Huda, it's the fucking *arnona*."

Samira paused before continuing. "See, habibti Huda, don't be so sad. We're not criminals, we're all heroes and heroes need energy, so here, have something sweet." Samira broke into a nervous laugh as she spread a large spoonful of orange marmalade on a tiny piece of bread. "Here, Huda, try this marmalade, it's truly good. The only thing I'll miss if I ever make it out of this damn place is their damn good marmalades and jams."

And then the chomping started all over again: mtaa ... mtaa ... mtaa...

At this point Huda pressed her right ear against the dirty mattress (which also smelled), her right palm still covering her nostrils, while her left palm pressed against her left ear. They must have placed her with Samira as part of her punishment. She found herself seriously considering quitting her repetitive visits to her father's house in West Jerusalem.

Huda felt that the only way she could end the saga of the

morning egg stench and Samira's loud munching and licking of marmalade off her sticky fingers was by resuming their pre-breakfast conversation. Despite her great discomfort she sat up on her mattress. "Once I'm done with the Israeli trial, hopefully soon, I'll have to go home and face another two harsh trials: one from my son Hani, and another from my mother, Bakiza. They both get so mad at me whenever I visit my father's house in the Greek Colony, and I do that almost every week …"

Samira could not keep quiet any longer and interrupted, "Yakhti (sister), what use is it visiting your father's house in West Jerusalem? You see what happens to you when the Jewish family calls the police and complains, all it takes the Balloons family, or whatever their name is, is to make a …"

"The Blumbergs," Huda corrected her. Samira gave her a blank look before continuing, "Whatever their name is, for the Jewish Balloon family it's only a matter of a phone call; but for you and your family it's a big headache. And look at you: a nice, elegant, respectable lady thrown into prison, and for what? Tell me, for what? We can hardly keep our houses in East Jerusalem, let alone West Jerusalem. Come on, forget your house in West Jerusalem, that's over with, khalas, enough, 1948 is history."

At this Huda could not help but remember the Israeli officer who had interrogated her only a few weeks ago. "Stop living in the past, that's your problem. You Arabs continue to live in the past," he had lectured her with growing impatience. "Wake up, it's 2011, not 1948. Khalas, Huda, khalas, it's all over," he had shouted at her.

His words echoed in her ears. For a fraction of a second a terrible thought flashed across her mind: could it be that Samira was an *asfourah*,[13] a bird, an informer? As far as Huda knew, no

---

[13] *Asfourah* in Arabic literally means a bird, and in this context, an informer. It is a common practice in Israeli prisons to extract information before interrogations or court trials by planting informers amongst detainees.

one was kept that long in the Russian Compound which functioned mostly as an interrogation centre rather than a long-term prison. But she quickly convinced herself and dismissed these paranoid suspicions regarding her innocent cellmate. She continued, "My Mama is truly terrified that if I keep visiting our house in the West and keep bugging the Blumbergs, the Israeli officials will ultimately punish me by throwing us out of our house in East Jerusalem. I mean not only me, but my son Hani and my mother as well."

"Your mother is certainly right on this one, Huda, you should know better. They've done that many times already: didn't they evict the Ghawi and Hannoun families from Sheikh Jarrah, your neighbourhood? Isn't that where you live? They also evicted the al-Kurd family from their house in Wadi al-Jouz. Poor Abu Kamel, he couldn't bear being thrown out, he ended up with a stroke that finished him off, right then and there. Look at his poor wife, Umm Kamel: she squatted in a tent next to her house, then what? Six months later, only God knows where they took her. The *msakhameh*, poor thing, she ended up with no husband and no house. Huda, listen to me, they won't rest till they get rid of all of us Arabs in East Jerusalem. So stop being silly, visiting your '48 house in Jewish Jerusalem. It's no use, believe me, no use. I'm surprised that an educated woman like you gets herself into so much trouble. Sorry, habibti, I don't understand why you go looking for trouble. Do you need more problems to add to the ones they create for us every single day?"

Huda kept quiet, thinking to herself, "How can I explain to Samira the vow I made to myself to visit my father's house in West Jerusalem as often as I could, for as long as I live? The vow I made forty-five years ago, on June 7, 1967, when I saw Baba's tears rolling down his cheeks. How can I explain to Samira what an obsession is? How can I explain that one does not control an obsession, it's the other way round, it's the obsession that takes hold of you? Huda sensed that she was becoming obsessed with her obsession. How can I admit to a stranger, who may be an informer, how taxing and painful it has been to keep true to a vow? Oh, how I wish I could be indifferent! How I wish I could get away from it all, living in Amman, Beirut, Dubai, San Francisco or Australia like so many others, including my own sister and brothers.

But don't we carry all that baggage with us wherever we go? Was I making those visits for myself or for Baba? If for my own sake, then I'm tired of it all, and if for my late father's sake, then that's become a real burden: Baba, is it at all fair that you pass away thirty years ago and leave me with this weight to carry? Every day I ask myself, why am I doing this?

Has this become a vendetta between me and the Jewish family that lives in our house?

Between me and the police officer who keeps arresting me?

Whatever it is, and for whatever reason, I am so damn exhausted!

Huda broke down crying.

Or was it *all* the fault of that little dog that incessantly barked and snarled at us when we went to visit our house for the very first time? Huda thought of that nasty little dog and then smiled.

"Huda! For God's sake, why are you crying? You cry and smile all at the same time. Explain to me why you go there and get yourself into trouble?" Samira's question halted Huda's thoughts. It took her a while to remember what Samira's question was. Then she said, "Listen to yourself, Samira; you and my mother and Hani are all harder on me than the Israelis themselves."

"No, no, habibti, you're wrong on this one. There is no one on the surface of this planet crueller to us than the bloody Israelis. Look what they've done to me. They ..." Huda had already heard Samira's story, at great length and in minute detail, started

129

the very minute the warden clicked open the iron door and pushed Huda into Samira's tiny sphere. But that did not stop her from repeating it for the third time in less than fifteen hours. Yet this third edition included some new facts.

"Listen to what the bastards, *il arsat*, excuse my language Sitt Huda, did to me. A week after I had settled with them and paid the thirty-five thousand shekels ($10,000) for the house *arnona*, they came back demanding I pay the television *arnona* for the last five years. They insisted that I had to pay another ten thousand shekels ($3,000)! After having paid every last penny I had and more for the house *arnona*, where would I get more money? You tell me. I told the officer, even if you try to sell me body and soul in Suq al-khurdah (flea market) you will not get a thousand shekels." Huda couldn't help giggling as did Samira, without the slightest pause in her story.

"I told the damn Israeli officer who came to check on the contents of my house that it wasn't me but my brother Ali who bought the TV set. I didn't want a TV in the first place. Ali bought it then went to Detroit. He never sent me a single penny and now you want me to pay his TV tax! The officer said that if I didn't pay the tax they would take away the TV. Sure enough the bastard walked off with my TV on his hip, but not before he threatened to come back in two weeks if I didn't pay up. And sure enough, there he was on my doorstep two weeks later and this time he brought along two big men who carried away my fridge; a week later, my washing machine; then my living room furniture; then my bed and closet with all my clothes in it. Then, two months later when I still couldn't pay, they finally came and carried me away. And here I am in prison until Allah *yifrijah*, until I get released from jail and my troubles. How? Don't ask me."

While Samira went on with her *arnona* saga it dawned on Huda that perhaps *arnona* was the most-used word by

Palestinians in East Jerusalem. *Arnona* this and *arnona* that is all one hears in the streets, on buses, at home, work and even at demonstrations. Perhaps the Jerusalem *arnona* had become a main cause of the "the crazed of Jerusalem"[14] syndrome.

Samira was still talking. "Sometimes I take it easy on myself by swearing to God, *wallahi*, it's better for me to stay here in this cell. They do all the shopping for me; they do all the shopping, cooking and dish-washing for me, the only thing I miss is my mattress. I once joked with the Israeli officer, telling him that if they planned on keeping me here long enough they could at least give me back my good mattress. You know what the bastard replied? 'Instead of us giving you back your mattress why don't you get your rich cousin Anis to bail you out.' *Fil mishmesh*, in your dreams. I tell you, Huda, with the service-free *arnona* they impose on us and the many fines and penalties we East Jerusalem Arabs pay them, we've become the casino where they always win ... or even better, the *baqara* Holandiyeh (Dutch cow) that they continue to milk."

Only when Samira stopped to take a deep breath did Huda notice that her eyes were brimming with tears. She couldn't tell whether Samira was laughing or weeping.

"*Sharu il baliyyat ma yudhek*, the worst disaster is that which makes you laugh," Samira concluded before finally sinking into a deep silence. Slowly she slid against the iron bars behind her and squatted on the floor.

Huda looked closely at Samira's worn-out face and thought how young and fortunate she was by comparison. A whole city seemed sunk in the deep cracks of Samira's wrinkled face.

It made Huda think how fatigued her beloved city was. Made her think of all the worn-out Jerusalemite faces around her: her

---

[14] The term "the crazed of Jerusalem" refers to the noticeably numerous mentally or psychologically distressed persons walking the streets of Jerusalem.

young son Hani, her ageing mother Bakiza, all her relatives, most of her friends, the neighbours, her colleagues at the university, certainly the students and every shop-keeper she knew, inside or outside the city walls where she lived and worked.

Every single person she knew in East Jerusalem had an ongoing exhausting saga with the Israelis. They were all trying hard to hang in there.

Like Samira, Huda started counting them and their problems, one by one:

Musa, whose family had always lived in Jerusalem, where he himself was born and raised and now, only because he had married Lisa, an Englishwoman, he had to fight the Israelis day and night to keep his Jerusalem residency.

Rema, and the agonising process of renewing her Jerusalem ID every single year.

Nurjihan, who cannot have her Ramallah husband, Khaldun, live with her and their kids in Jerusalem.

Two-year old Qaisar, who has been deprived of his Jerusalem ID because his mother was from Jerusalem while his father was from the West Bank.

Hidaya and Ribhi, who were forced to close a century-old business, the famed National Hotel, due to impossible debts and *arnona* problems.

Huda's own sister and three brothers who had lost their Jerusalem ID cards simply because they stayed abroad longer than two years.

All those whose houses have been demolished, the ones Samira had mentioned and more: the Ghawis, the Kurdis and the Hannouns, as well as the twenty-two Arab families living in Sheikh Jarrah who have been given eviction orders.

She thought of the city itself: the "capital" that had lost all its Arab suburbs because of a monstrous concrete wall that had been built around it.

A city that has been isolated from its Arab surroundings, the West Bank and Gaza.

As the list got longer and longer Huda started wondering whether she, like Samira, would not mind spending a few weeks in prison, away from it all.

God, is this troubled place truly your Holy City?

At that very moment Huda's daydream (or nightmare) came to an end. She heard her name called by the prison warden. By the time he appeared and clicked open the iron door to their tiny cell, Huda, like an obedient soldier, had stood up to her full height.

"Huda."

"Yes," she replied promptly.

"Follow me."

Wearily, Huda dragged her chained feet, and taking small steps came up close to Samira and kissed her on both cheeks. It felt like she had been Samira's mate for sixteen years rather than sixteen hours.

"Good luck, Huda. I know for a fact that you'll keep visiting your family house in West Jerusalem, but remember, it's far more important that you protect your Sheikh Jarrah house."

Huda smiled.

Samira leaned against the shut iron door, waiting for the next delivery.

13

The Iraqi Officer

"**H**uda! One more visit and you'll be deported, do you understand what I'm saying?" He shouted at her in Hebrew.

She reminded him that she neither spoke nor understood Hebrew. He shifted to Arabic, her mother tongue and perhaps his as well.

"Huda! *Il marrah il jay ib'aad, mafhoum?*" he repeated in Arabic with an Iraqi accent.

He called her by her first name, Huda.

She argued back with familiarity and no inhibitions.

Stop going there.

Leave those people alone.

Leave them in peace.

Stop terrifying them.

The police officer formulated his statement in as many ways and forms as possible. "You're terrorising them, do you realise that?" The more he explained the happier and more satisfied she felt.

"Do you have any idea what these people think or how they feel whenever you appear there?" He looked Huda straight in the eye.

"And *how* do they feel, Captain Ya'kov?" she answered back, then cracked a mysterious Mona Lisa smile. "And what do *they* think?"

"You are not allowed to appear on their doorstep anymore," he snapped back. Anticipating and refusing to hear the response she often gave him, as they already had a long history of interrogations, he continued, "Now you listen to me carefully. You are not to go there again. You are not to set foot on their doorstep. You are not to enter their garden."

"I no longer tread on the doorstep nor do I enter the garden," she almost parroted, making sure to use the article 'the' and not 'their'.

"Do I need to remind you that not so long ago you went into the garden and picked pomegranates?"

"Wouldn't you pick pomegranates off the tree your father planted?" She flashed him a big smile this time.

He stared at her shining brown eyes, saw her familiar mischievous smile, then assumed a pose not unlike Rodin's Thinker before saying wearily and yet firmly, "In the past it was your father's house; today it is not."

"Today it is not." Huda mechanically repeated after him, then added, "Why not?"

"Why not what?"

"Why is it no longer my father's house?" she hesitated before adding "mine".

"Huda, I hope you realise that you are in the Moriaya Police Station, and more specifically, in *prison*," he emphasised. "You are not in the History Department at Al Quds University or at Mount Scopus.[15]

He broke into loud, self-satisfied laughter.

Wanting to ease the tension to her advantage, Huda pretended to join in in the laughter.

---

[15] Mount Scopus in this context refers to a part of the Hebrew University located on Mount Scopus in East Jerusalem. It constitutes an enclave that continued to be under Israeli control between 1948 and 1967.

"Huda, by now you should know that this is absentee property and that nothing has changed since I saw you last, which was less than a month ago."

"Do I look like an absentee to you? Is it a crime for an absentee, or a ghost, to visit their father's garden? Are you arresting a ghost?"

"Your ghosts are worse than your real selves!" he retorted, rolling his eyes.

Considering the unbearable presence of her father's ghost, Huda totally agreed with the officer's comment. The presence of the absent could indeed be agonising.

Captain Ya'kov's patience was reaching its limit. "Alright, enough!" His eyes opened wide. "And stop living in the past. That is your problem. You Arabs continue to live in the past."

"When it comes to Jews, you have a two-thousand-year memory, but when it comes to us Palestinians, you have a sixty-year amnesia."

Even though dealing with Huda's obsession was much less dangerous than dealing with the many drug and criminal cases waiting for him downstairs, he did not want to spend any more time on the Imam's house.

Captain Ya'kov gave his final verdict yet again: "Huda, next time we receive a phone call from Yo'av or any other member of the Blumberg family complaining about you being at their doorstep, or that you're in their garden picking lemons or pomegranates or in front of that house, or even across the street from it, I will throw you in prison, take you to court, and prosecute until you're deported."

As with all Palestinians, the *deportation* word chilled Huda to the bone.

Realising that he had finally taken control of the situation, the officer repeated: "Next time deportation, Huda. *Ib'aad!*" he yelled in Arabic.

Terrified, Huda kept quiet.

Disconcerted by her unusual silence, Captain Ya'kov stood up, went around his desk, came up to Huda and removed her handcuffs.

Part Four

Elie: A Bird's-eye View

14

A Businessman from Tel Aviv

Elie was sipping the very last drops of his digestif when we walked into the trattoria. He greeted us enthusiastically, "Fantastiques, marveilleuse, délicieux." Why in French? First, because he had grown up in Lebanon and second, because he has been living in Paris since 1982.

Everything about Elie – his beaming face, flushed chubby cheeks, drooping eyelids, and most noticeably the huge serviette wrapped around his neck – indicated his indulgence in the too-many-course meal: *l'anti pasto, il primo piatto, il secondo, il contorno, il dolce, il vino*, even *l'aqua minerale* Badoid.

The four of us, the renowned Palestinian economist and writer, Jamil Hilal, his Italian wife Piera, a development specialist, Anna, an Italian journalist and I, eagerly followed the waitress who seated us in an alcove with only one table. The young waitress handed each one of us a menu and disappeared swiftly.

Unlike Elie who had the time to enjoy his elaborate meal, we had to rush. For in less than an hour we were to attend Elie's presentation on the late Palestinian poet, Mahmoud Darwish. Once each of us had made her/his selections from a long list of mouth-watering possibilities, I hurried out of our hidden alcove in search of the waitress, lost among the buzzing tables of loud and noisy customers.

I was more than happy to practice my Italian. I wanted to alert our waitress to the fact that we were in a hurry. To make sure I got it right I divided my request into two simple short sentences: first, "the four of us want to eat," and second: "we're in a hurry". And since eating in a hurry is not exactly a tradition or a norm in an Italian restaurant, I tried to emphasise the hurry part: "*Siamo in fritta*" and then, "*Vogliamo quattro persone per mangiare.*"

The waitress who had been very polite until then said, "You can start by eating me and my friend Francesca," pointing to the waitress standing next to her, "And I shall run and get you two more people to eat." She then called out, "*Alberto e Alessandro venite qui subito,*" come here quickly. I later learnt that I had said: "We are being fried and we would like to eat four people."

Soon, we were swallowing our *tartufo* (truffle) pasta and *tartufo* gnocchi and the excellent corposo red wine recommended by Elie, who had meanwhile joined our table and asked the waitress for a wine glass. Knowing what a gourmet Elie is, I made exactly the same choice of plates that he had ordered and so obviously enjoyed.

I had done the same thing the day before when I encountered Elie wandering in Bellinzona's food market – this at a time when he and I were supposed to be at the Teatro Sociale where the Babel literary festival events on Palestine were taking place.

I hope you understand why a Palestinian has no desire to attend anything Palestinian (or on Palestine), but opts instead for the food market. Elie was standing in front of a cheese stall tasting a dark red cheese, then a dark yellow one. After an elaborate process of cheese selecting, tasting and chewing, his facial expression, as well as the continuous nodding of his head, indicated Elie's full satisfaction. In addition to the red wine cheese and the yellow beer cheese, he sampled a third, and then a fourth.

I must say that I didn't find the idea of beer cheese or wine cheese particularly appealing, but having so much confidence in, and appreciation of, gourmets like Elie, I ended up buying whatever he bought.

With a mother like mine who, when she failed to institute a food-for-lipstick barter programme in Amman similar to that established with Umm Samir in Jerusalem, fed her four kids and husband out-of-the-can green peas and Uncle Ben's rice, it is no wonder that I developed a fetish for gourmet food and gourmet friends. Not only did she hardly cook anything else, but Mama managed to build a whole myth, which sadly I believed for the longest time, that preparing good rice is one of the *most* difficult tasks in gourmet cooking. And since she did that, day in and day out, she had qualified herself as an out-standing cook.

May God rest her soul, but what a gastronomic tragedy it all was!

Since I was enjoying the delicious *tartufo* pasta, I saw no point in thinking further about my mother's tasteless cooking. And since I can never keep quiet for long, I asked Elie if he was ready for his presentation on Darwish in less than half an hour. In response to my question Elie responded with a smile that spread from ear to ear and across his full cheeks that were flushed almost to the same tint as the red wine he was still sipping. He gave me a mischievous look through his thick round glasses, then giggled and answered, "Suad, do you know the Arabic expression "*Jai u jaieb 'edet il naseb ma'uh*" (he arrived with his bluffing tool-kit). He meant that he had made people believe that he had become *the* expert on Mahmoud Darwish. Needless to say, Elie had done the best translation from Arabic to French that many experts consider the *very* best translation ever made of Darwish's poetry in any language.

Even though I must have heard this expression numerous

times before, it was only then that I realised how humorous and original it was. I imagined an enormous man, as huge as Elie himself, carrying a gigantic box, but unlike Pandora's box with all the evils of the world, Elie's bluffing-box contained a stock of fine words, well-turned phrases, striking images, and scraps of poetry and elegant prose. With these he would soon captivate his audience, the way his reference to the bluffing-box had captivated me.

Although I was sitting next to Elie, I somehow missed the beginning of another story he had started telling Jamil, who was seated at the other end of the table. Jamil was savouring his *cinghiale* (wild boar).

"*Mais bien sûr*, yes, they sold him the air."

"What! They sold him the air, the sky, the space above your own house!" Jamil almost choked on his *cinghiale*.

"Yes, they claim that the air above my house is not mine but theirs, so they gave the 'building air rights', i.e. the right to construct a high-rise building on top of my two-storey house, to a businessman from Tel Aviv."

Totally puzzled, I had to interrupt Elie.

"Wait, wait, wait! Elie, I am truly sorry but I missed the beginning of your story. Now, who is selling what?" I demanded.

"I am talking about my house in Haifa. You know I own a house in Haifa, don't you?" Elie asked in the same animated manner he had used when discussing cheese and wine.

"Of course, I know that you own a house in Haifa."

Prolific writer though he is, I, like many others, have read, heard about, or seen all that Elie has written throughout his life. So I was aware that his family is from Haifa and that in 1948, when Elie was two and a half, his family had fled to Lebanon and he had grown up in Beirut. In the early Seventies he went to study in France and then returned to Beirut only to leave it again right after the Israeli invasion of Lebanon in 1982. He has been living permanently in Paris since then. But I must say that

144

this was the very first time I had heard him talk about his house in Haifa.

I was gratified to hear Elie use the personal pronouns *I* and *my*. The Israelis think that with time (as the Palestinian Nakba generation disappears) their grabbing of Arab properties will become easier, or be accomplished de facto.

Time makes Palestinians forget.

Time makes Jews remember.

"Yes, what about your house in Haifa?" I was very curious to know.

Elie took a Montblanc pen out of his pocket and started sketching a diagram of his house on my yellow paper placemat. I pushed my *tartufo* plate aside to make room for his house in Haifa.

"My house is in al Hadar, il Carmel, so it is on a very steep slope." In Picasso-like freehand, Elie drew two parallel lines and connected them with a curved arrow indicating a steep slope. Actually the word *hadar* is probably Hebrew for the Arabic *munhadar* meaning the steep slope. But, like everything else, they have eaten the *mun.*

"Yes, I know it is very steep," I said to assure Elie that I was listening attentively to him. I was now also following his words as an architect.

"You see, the Israeli Custodian of Palestinian Absentee Property had forbidden the Arab tenants who live in my house from making any repairs to the building over the years." I knew this, and I also knew that the prohibition against maintaining Arab property applied to both Arab landlords and their tenants.

While Elie was totally absorbed in drawing an elongated cube that represented his house, I relished the fact that the users, tenants and occupants – all those benefitting from Elie's house in Haifa – are indeed Arabs and not, as is often the case, Israelis.

"Thank God that the people living in your house are Palestinians."

145

"Yes, they're Palestinians from the village of Fassoutah," Elie responded, while still concentrating on the rough sketch of his house in Haifa. He added a three-arched gallery (*riwaq*) to the lower level of the cube, a large rectangular opening indicating a terrace on the second floor, and two small windows on either side. Across the right side of the cube he drew two parallel inclined lines indicating a staircase connecting the two floors.

While still sketching Elie resumed his story, "As a result of the Israeli policy, the tenants could not repair the staircase leading to the house and so the stairs collapsed. This meant that the tenants could no longer get to the second floor from the garden. They now reach it from the upper road."

Here Elie added two straight arrows indicating the new entrance: a bridge connecting the house with the upper road.

I was a bit confused as to how the residents managed to get into the house from the back street, but I did not allow my obsession with technical details to distract me or Elie from the story.

"One day Muntaser, my tenant, called me from Haifa to tell me that he had recently received a letter from the Israeli Custodian of Absentee Property informing him that they have sold the air, the air rights, the air space above my house, to a businessman from Tel Aviv who had plans to build a high-rise on top of my two-storey house." Elie stopped, took a deep breath, several sips of wine, followed by his usual "Bien sûr!" and a big smile.

I do not know what it is about Palestinians that makes them smile or even laugh at a time when they should be crying.

At this point Elie vertically extended the dimensions of his cubic house, indicating the future high-rise planned by the businessman from Tel Aviv. He then raised his head waiting for our feedback.

"*Veramente fanculo,*" said Anna. See how expressive Italian can be!

146

Jamil went into a fit of laughter, which was infectious.

"Are you sure that the man from Tel Aviv is a businessman and not an astronaut?" A typical Jamil comment.

"*Bien sûr … bien sûr*, an Israeli businessman from Tel Aviv," Elie confirmed.

The animated discussion fell into a deep silence, which was soon broken by Piera's question, "Suad, who normally owns or has the air space above a building?"

I must admit I was extremely challenged by her question. "Hmm, well … let's see … it all depends … *theoretically* it all depends on the building regulations of the Municipality of Haifa. If the building law allows four floors then you, Elie, have the right to add another two floors; if the law allows for seven or eight floors then again you have the right to build that many floors. If your house was in Manhattan, then you would have the right to build up to a hundred or a hundred and twenty floors. It all depends on the zoning and building regulations of the Haifa Municipality."

I was responding as if the Israelis were normal people in a normal country.

Oh God, I thought, Israeli actions on the ground are challenging enough, but now we have to deal with their absurdities in the skies too! My mind was already occupied trying to figure out the ingenuity of suspending that bloody high-rise building from the skies without touching the ground.

I was so challenged by all this that I was about to admit to Elie and the others that, as an architecture student, I had failed *all* structural courses, but thank God Jamil saved me from that embarrassment.

"Wait until they claim underground rights and start building parking garages or tunnels below your property, then your two-floor house will become a falafel sandwiched between their two claimed rights to heaven and hell," Jamil said.

"Air rights might reasonably apply when it comes to security or flight zones, not when it comes to building," I said, feeling the heavy weight of responsibility for making sense of Israeli ingenuity.

"Well, with Israel there are always original ideas when it comes to stripping Palestinians of their rights, whether on the ground, below ground, in the sea or, as now, in the air," said Jamil.

Obsessively trying to figure out how the structure of that danin high-rise would drop from the sky, I offered a hesitant thought: "But some structural elements of the new building will have to touch your land, unless they find a way to drop it from the air."

"Drop it from where?" asked Elie.

"From the sky."

"From God's seventh heaven."

"*Min 'ind Rabna*, from on high."

"Or from hell?"

I know for a fact that once we start being too dependent and demanding of God it means we have despaired.

And obviously we have lost hope.

Elie looked at his watch, got up and left hurriedly, leaving us all hanging in the air.

As I walked the rainy streets of Bellinzona I wondered: Was that heaviness I felt in my head caused by the *vino rosso corposo?*

Or by the Custodian of Absentee Property?

Or the result of contemplating the genius of the Businessman from Tel Aviv?

As I stepped into the Teatro Sociale I saw Elie under the orange stage lights. I took my seat, closed my eyes and listened to Elie's corposo voice:

"On this land there is something worth living for.
Mahmoud Darwish."

Part Five

Homage to My Mother-in-law
1911-2005

15

That Very Moment

She had never narrated *this particular story* before.
And I had never asked for it.

But this time I did.

Umm Salim must have been utterly surprised to hear me insist that she tell me, *in detail*, her 1948 story. I wanted to know everything about that day and *that very moment* when she, her husband Edmon, and their two-year-old son, Salim fled from their home in Jaffa.

My out-of-the-blue request perplexed my mother-in-law and made her a bit distrustful. She must have recalled the boredom on Salim's face and mine, whenever she told and retold stories about her childhood and youthful years in Jaffa. "We in Jaffa went to the sea every week-end, we in Jaffa had huge orange groves, we in Jaffa cooked this way; we in Jaffa often went shopping in Tel Aviv, *ihna ahel Yafa,* we Jaffa people did it this way … and we Jaffans did it that way …" and so on and so forth.

If you weren't from Jaffa, and many are not, you would certainly feel you had missed out on paradise, and had no place amongst the fortunate Jaffans. And many did.

I had realised only lately that in spite of the many stories she repeated over and over, my mother-in-law never mentioned anything about *that day.*

Of the day she left home and was never allowed back

She never said anything

And I never asked

But today was the very first time I was eager to have her tell her story and listen very carefully to every word she said. I wanted to make sure I would remember all that she had to tell me. I even recorded it.

It was the loss of my own mother two months earlier (February 27, 2005) that made me realise the need to listen *carefully* to my ninety-four-year-old mother-in-law. I was trying to compensate for the loss of my mother, and with her, the loss of the minute details of how the Jewish forces dragged my father's family, my aunt and uncle, out of their home in Jaffa, and how the intense shooting and the occupation of their house forced my parents to leave their home in Jerusalem.

What amazes me most is that we, as a people, have shared our collective story of being thrown out of our homeland, Palestine, with each other and with many others – actually we have bored the world with this collective story – but somehow the individual Palestinian shies away, or perhaps is too afraid, to share the very personal story of being thrown out of her or his home, living room, or bedroom. These personal stories are seldom told, not even to one's children, perhaps not even to oneself.

I guess the wound remains open.

But yet, even though Umm Salim lived in Ramallah for fifty-five years (1951–2005), I rarely heard her tell a story about her life in Ramallah or use the expression "we in Ramallah," the town in which she lived for over half a century; the town where she died at the age of ninety-four.

Though it was not her wish, Umm Salim was buried in Ramallah.

Jaffa in the 1940s

Having been married to her "adorable" and *only* son for the last twenty-one years (1984-2005) I knew by now that Umm Salim came from a big family. She had six brothers and one sister: "Me and Claire were treated like queens, particularly me. I was difficult and ..."

"Still are," I said jokingly (perhaps not so jokingly).

"I was difficult and fussy when it came to food," she continued.

"Only when it came to food!" I was taking advantage of the situation, but Umm Salim totally ignored my comments and carried on.

"My mother had two helpers, but she still had eight spoilt children and a very demanding husband. In spite of that, she managed to pamper each and every one of us: from little Qaisar (Ceasar) who once fell down the well, got diabetes as a result and died very young, to Najib, the eldest and most difficult. Najib was so fussy about his clothes, I can't tell you."

And of course, I can't tell you how many times Umm Salim had told me the same story over and over again. Not only that, but every time she mentioned her youngest brother Qaisar, she would add the refrain: poor thing he once fell down the well, became diabetic and died very young.

"In spite of everything, we were all extremely well-disciplined: no matter what, we all had to sit around the big dining table for the three meals of the day. I do not remember one time when we did not eat together: no one was allowed to come home late for lunch or dinner; they would not be fed if they did."

"Umm Salim ... It sounds very familiar!" Again she ignored me.

"Poor Mama, she would prepare a different dish for each one

153

of us: Najib did not eat meat, Claire did not like chicken, I couldn't stand spinach, Elias couldn't stand the smell of cabbage or cauliflower, Baba did not eat liver while Toni loved it, Qaisar [poor thing he once ...] was vegetarian, and so on and so on.

"Out of respect, all of us, except Mama, had to be seated at the table before Baba arrived exhausted from work. As soon as Mama heard his footsteps on the stairs she would run to open the door, welcome him, then help him take off his jacket or coat and hang it up for him. Mother would only sit after Baba had washed his face and hands and sat down at the head of the table.

"'Shsh, your father is tired, keep quiet.' We had to be quiet as long as Baba was at home, and remain completely silent for the duration of his two-hour siesta, which he took religiously every single afternoon of his life.

"However, I must say that the biggest shock of my life was when my schoolteacher inquired about my father's job. I had no clue. I came running home and asked Mama: 'What does Baba do for a living?' She looked me in the face and said with all seriousness, 'Your Baba is a landlord,' and when I asked what that entailed she said, 'He collects the rents at the end of every month or at the end of every year.' Expecting my teacher to inquire further, I asked Mama, 'And what does Baba do when he's not collecting rent once a month or once a year?' She answered, 'He spends the rest of his time in the coffee shop playing cards or *tawlet zaher*, backgammon, with other landlords.'

"Poor Mama, there she was, killing herself taking care of a family of ten while Baba was sitting in the coffee shop ... collecting rent from three shops and one house ... that must have been truly hard work!" Umm Salim broke into hearty laughter at this point.

"From that day on I never hushed for Baba or any other man in my whole life."

To me that was pretty obvious.

"Our Cirque Sportive club (in her French accent) in Jaffa was highly exclusive. It was reserved for *il Catolic only* (the Catholics). Not even Orthodox Christians were allowed in (not to mention Muslims). Remember Signore Alonzo?" she posed the question then carried on, "He was in charge of our club!"

Not wanting to spoil my mother-in-law's romanticised memories of Jaffa, I kept the response to myself. Of course I remembered Signore Alonzo. He was the one who, in 1981, became very reluctant to help me locate my father's house in the Manshiyeh neighbourhood of Jaffa the minute he realised that I was not a Christian.

"Down, down there …" he had said in a dismissive tone and an even more dismissive hand gesture. If Alonzo was in charge of the Cirque Sportive, of course no Muslim ever made it to the club.

It was such sectarian and class-conscious comments that made her secular leftist son, Salim, feel so embarrassed by what his mother said. He would often change the subject or simply roll his eyes and walk out of the room.

"I never wanted to marry. I never liked men. Actually, I was never attracted to men," Umm Salim said with a straight face. I smiled and kept quiet.

"Before Edmon and I were married, we went on a date to visit my brother Elias in Haifa. On the way there, all of a sudden Edmon grabbed me tightly and gave me a kiss."

Hmm … a kiss, I thought to myself, but before I had a chance to visualise or even romanticise about that very first kiss, Umm Salim went on, "And in return, he got a big slap on his face. 'Wow,' I said, 'who gave you permission to kiss me?' Edmon just smiled." My mother-in-law still burst out laughing whenever she recalled this slap-for-a-kiss exchange more than sixty years later.

155

But I must say that I was not at all surprised by this chaste episode. Ever since I have known her, my mother-in-law has never liked being kissed by anyone. I dare say not even by her own son. "Yech, I can't stand it when people kiss me, I don't know why they do that! Aren't they afraid of microbes?" she would say, rubbing the kiss off her cheek if, for one reason or another, she could not prevent that sudden Mediterranean exchange of two or three kisses in a row.

"Suad dear, make sure you have two separate beds, yech, I can't stand it when someone breathes in my face." That was the *very first* bit of advice my mother-in-law gave me when her adorable son and I were getting married.

And then she wondered why we never had children.

"Every summer all the girls and boys of our Cirque Sportive would go swimming in the sea. Often we got on a *hasakeh* (a kind of heavy, keeled surf board). A boy and a girl sat on each board; we girls sat in front while the boys sat behind with the double oars.

"We were in the middle of the sea when the boy behind me came up close, grabbed me and then circled my waist with his hands (meaning embraced her and gave her hug). I got so disgusted and panicky that I threatened to drown myself! This threw him into a panic and he instantly removed his hands."

"No slapping the face this time," I jested, and thought, poor boy. Then I remembered what Salim often repeated about his father, "*Miskeen* [poor] Baba."

When I asked her whether she remembered the boy's name she said, "No, why would I?" then continued, "I never liked it when boys touched me. It disgusted me. I was very strict."

"I bet not all the girls were as strict as you were, Umm Salim!" I teased. She instantly replied, "*Nooo*, no, of course not. There were these two naughty girls who would often squeeze Edmon between them until he blushed and turned all red … poor thing, he was extremely shy."

156

With a mother-in-law who didn't like boys to touch her and a shrinking violet for a husband, I always wondered how my own husband Salim made it into this world.

It was not the first time that I'd heard my mother-in-law tell this story, of course. Like most of her Jaffa tales, she repeated it again and again whenever she had a listening ear, rarely mine and hardly ever Salim's.

The baker who fled town
May 14, 1948

She never narrated *this particular story* and I had never asked.

But this time I did.

"It wasn't until that early morning when Milaneh, our housemaid, came back with the unbaked dough that I realised it was no longer possible for us to stay in our home," said Umm Salim.

"'The baker fled town last night,' announced Milaneh."

Knowing how well my mother-in-law cooked and baked, I was not entirely convinced that one would flee one's house, one's beloved town and one's own country because the baker had left. She must have seen the disbelief on my face, so she tried to give a more convincing account.

"Well, the day before our house had been hit badly from that side," she raised her head and pointed, with stretched arm and upper body, to the ceiling of her Ramallah house. "I mean from the direction of Tel Aviv, from where all the shooting was coming. There was also no water, no telephone lines, and perhaps no electricity; I can't really remember whether we had electricity at that point or not. All I recall is that we painted all the glass in our windows navy blue during the 1948 war."

She paused for a second and then continued: "Edmon was *adamant* not to leave home. We were planning to stay put even though most members of both our families had already left for

157

Beirut weeks earlier. As you know, our families used to go to Mount Lebanon every summer but that year, because of the war, they had gone a month or two earlier, except for my brother Fu'ad, who stayed behind to look after my parents' house and Baba's businesses, and Abdallah, Edmon's brother, who also stayed behind with his wife Julia to take care of their house. As you know, Suad, many houses were broken into and robbed." Having been born a few years after the war I knew nothing, of course, but kept quiet.

"Edmon was the *inspecteur* [I could not but smile as her French accent reminded me of Inspecteur Clouseau] of Socony-Vacuum which later became Mobil Oil. Therefore he and I knew well that the rumours about the shortage in petrol, which would soon make it impossible to escape the heavily bombarded city, were actually true. Being in charge of all Socony-Vacuum employees as well as their cars, Edmon had given *strict* instructions to all to stay put. So how could *we* leave them behind?" Umm Salim asked in a responsible voice, some fifty-seven years later.

Until the day she died, October 30, 2005, Umm Salim received a monthly pension from Mobil Oil, now Exxon Mobil.

"That week all of Jaffa, but mostly our neighbourhood, al Ajami, was badly hit by intensified shelling from Tel Aviv. The day before we left, all the Socony-Vacuum employees who worked under Edmon came to inform him that they had made up their minds. The situation had become unbearably dangerous so they and their families were leaving town. They also admitted to their boss that, behind his back, they had been storing gallons and gallons of petrol in order to drive themselves and their families to Beirut. They were going to hand in the cars to the Socony-Vacuum main offices in Beirut."

Realising the limitation of his authority over the destinies of his employees and their terrified families, Edmon then asked them for a few gallons of petrol for his own car.

At the break of dawn

"It was very early in the morning when we left. Milaneh made the coffee, got Salim dressed, and off we went to Beirut via Ramallah with our suitcases. Edmon, Salim and I, Milaneh stayed behind."

End of story.

She had never told *this story* before and I had never asked.

But this time I insisted she tell it to me *in detail.*

Like many 'historic moments', that night acquired significance retrospectively, when they realised they would not be allowed to go back home.

She looked at me, flashed me a subtle smile, stared straight ahead, then began talking:

"All I remember about *that* night is that it was long and humid, with a deadly silence broken only by erratic shooting. Edmon and I alternated tossing in bed."

"And then?"

"At the break of dawn Milaneh knocked at our bedroom door. Sensing that we had not slept that night, she hurried straightaway to the kitchen, made us coffee, a large pot of coffee and some sandwiches, and then went to get Salim ready. I got out of bed and slipped into the clothes I had put out the night before. Without uttering a word, Edmon did the same."

Knowing well how much time my match-it-all, elegant mother-in-law needed to get herself ready, it was not easy for me to visualise the slipping-into-her-clothes scene. And I could not help but be frivolous and think of those stale-bread sandwiches. Not realising that she would not set foot in her home ever again, I am sure slipping into her clothes and eating sandwiches made with stale bread were the real Nakba for my fussy gourmet mother-in-law.

"Being anxious about leaving, neither of us was up to breakfast. Without sitting down we each took a few quick sips of coffee, placed our half-full cups on the living room table and hurriedly left the room. While I carefully carried Salim down the two flights of stairs, Edmon and Milaneh brought down the heavy suitcases. With Milaneh's help, Edmon loaded the suitcases in the trunk, then cautiously and swiftly slipped into the driver's seat. I settled down in the passenger seat next to Edmon, with a cranky Salim on my lap."

I was about to beg my mother-in-law to sit in the back seat with my two-year-old husband, but since they were both safe and sound now, she at the age of ninety-four, he at sixty, it seemed an utterly unnecessary piece of cautionary advice.

"We said goodbye to Milaneh who promised to take care of the house. We had boarded up its windows and doors with thick wooden planks the day before."

Umm Salim must have noticed me looking unhappy at the thought of leaving Milaneh behind in an empty house in a deserted city, so she added:

"Milaneh was to leave the next day on a boat which would bring her and her family to Beirut. And since there was a shortage of boats as thousands of people had waited for days on end on the shores of Jaffa in order to be picked up, I asked my cousin Habib Ghandur, whose family owned a *bawabir* (boat) company to hurry up and bring more boats."

I must say that Umm Salim did not seem to be bothered by leaving her maid behind.

To avoid the guilty or innocent question I asked: "Umm Salim, what did you take with you when you left home?"

"Not much, just summer clothes. At the time we didn't realise that *this would be it*. If I had known I would have carried a wedding present: the silver make-up set given to me by my woman friends. It was truly beautiful." There was a long pause before Umm Salim continued, "Actually all the furniture in our house was brand new and beautiful."

160

A longer pause.

"Since the government [British] had taken every vacant house for its own employees, there was a severe shortage of houses. And since I adamantly *refused* to live with my in-laws …" Without meaning to, the words escaped my mouth, "Lucky in-laws", but Umm Salim was preoccupied with her own story:

"Edmon and I were engaged for three long years during which we carefully selected every single item and stacked it in a room at my in-laws', until one day we heard of an unoccupied house, and in agreement with its owners, we sneaked in late at night and arranged the furniture in all the rooms.

"As long as I live I shall never forget that night. The house looked fabulous the next day: I tell you, the dining table was *very* special. To this day I haven't seen anything like it. It had three curves at each end, and when extended it was just beautiful. We had bought it from a furniture shop in Tel Aviv, but it had been brought by the *Mascob* from Russia." At this point I could just see Umm Salim going from one room to another in her house in Jaffa, admiring her furniture. After a long pause she looked at the low coffee table on which we had placed our coffee cups.

"The coffee table was just gorgeous, most coffee tables then had square and bulky legs, but this one had very thin and elegant ones, delicately curved. Suad, let me show you what I mean." Umm Salim stood up, took me by the hand and led me to the guest room.

"See how beautiful and thin her legs are (tables happen to be feminine in Arabic), have you ever seen anything like this?" she was gazing at the coffee table in the middle of the room.

My mother-in-law's sensual description of the coffee table legs sounded more like a description of a gorgeous female-lover she had left behind in Jaffa. Her not liking boys touching her, and now these erotic descriptions of a (feminine) table made me suspect my mother-in-law's lesbian tendencies.

"Did you end up bringing *her,* I mean the table, with you to Ramallah, Umm Salim?"

"No, no ... but I had it made again by the same carpenter who had also fled Jaffa for Beirut."

I had tears in my eyes. I felt so bad that in all these years I had never noticed either the coffee table or its shapely, slender legs.

"Every single carpenter in Ramallah has come to see her elegant and beautifully curved legs," she added as she walked back to the glazed veranda of her Ramallah house.

I was gazing out of her window at Arafat's mausoleum when she spoke again: "I think Salim was about two and a half when we left Jaffa. He was born August 2nd, 1945. I got pregnant right away, I think the night we got married."

I could not help but think that she wanted to get it over with as quickly as possible. "And I bet that was about the only time you allowed Abu Salim, Edmon, to touch you."

She cracked up laughing, "*Ta'riban,* just about."

"No wonder you had only *one* child, but that was pretty efficient." I had a feeling that my mother-in-law liked talking about lost sex more than a lost house or a lost country.

"Mother, were you aware then that Salim was born in the same year, the same month, even the same day as the bombing of Hiroshima?" I interrupted.

"Hiroshima? Oh, yes," she replied indifferently.

She had never narrated *this particular story* before and I had never asked.

But this time I insisted she tell me *in detail*: "And then?"

"Soon we were near Edmon's brother's house ... hmm ... what was his name? You see, I forget these days. Oh yes, Abdallah. On the way to Abdallah's house we saw many deserted cars and trucks loaded with people's belongings and furniture. Some had been shelled but others were abandoned because they had run out of petrol. People were carrying their blankets and belongings and walking towards the seashore; many slept there for days on end. When we got to Abdallah's house to tell him that we were leaving, to say goodbye, he, his wife Julia, and his son Elias were in total panic.

"'Oh, *no* … we're *not* staying behind all by ourselves, the whole family has already left … please wait … wait, we're coming with you,' Abdullah begged.

"'But we don't have place for you in the car, we've got a few gallons of petrol in the back seat,' I said. 'Don't worry, Marie. Julia, Elias and I will put the petrol on our laps,' Abdallah insisted.

"'But that is dangerous and stupid!' I screamed back at him.

"'Certainly not as dangerous as staying behind all alone. You saw how much shooting and shelling there's been from Tel Aviv in the last few days.' Both Elias and Julia were hurriedly collecting a few personal belongings as Abdallah argued with me. Poor Edmon, he kept quiet. Well, ultimately I gave in," said Umm Salim.

"Eventually we drove away with an overcrowded car: Salim in my lap, a gallon of petrol in Abdallah's lap, another in Julia's, and a third in seventeen-year-old Elias'."

At that point, I was getting more interested in family gossip: "Come on, Umm Salim, it had nothing to do with having or not having room in your car. Admit it, you never liked Julia or Abdallah." I was purposely abusing my insider information to instigate more vicious family gossip, and I got it.

"Actually, I didn't mind Julia, she was naïve and stupid. It was Abdallah's guts I couldn't stand. He was such a Don Juan. Julia was filthy rich. Her family had so much gold they hoarded it in jars. Abdallah spent all her money travelling abroad, to Lebanon and Europe, having a good time all by himself he claimed, while flirting with all sorts of women. Then, as if she were a little girl, he would bring his wife a pretty *burnita* (hat) with a ribbon.

She would proudly go around town wearing it and bragging about her husband's love and the silly presents he gave her. *Aaah, I never liked the way he treated his wife.*"

I must say, at moments like these, I suspected that my mother-in-law was an earlier Simone de Beauvoir of the Arab world with no first or second sex.

"And …?" I insisted.

"A few weeks later I went to check on Milaneh. She was quarantined at the port in Beirut. 'Madame, stay away from me, don't come any closer,' she said when I greeted her from a distance."

Knowing my mother-in-law's hypochondria I was not worried about her getting any closer to Milaneh. Actually I was surprised she went to the Quarantine Bay in the first place, but household help was essential for my mother-in-law.

"'We've been contaminated by microbes. We must've picked up some disease on the overcrowded boat which carried us from Jaffa to Beirut. The Lebanese have decided to keep us in quarantine for forty days.'"

After a short pause Umm Salim continued:

"During that same visit, Milaneh gave me the bad news that our house was robbed the very day we left it. It seems that all the effort we put into nailing wooden planks on all the windows had been useless."

I must say that I was profoundly disturbed by the robbery in my in-laws' house, even though it had happened so many decades ago. It made me so angry, it felt as if it was happening today.

Pain and loss have no logic.

"Come, Suad, let me show you *the one* thing I still have from our house in Jaffa."

Umm Salim stood up, gripping my arm tightly. I followed. She walked into the corridor leading to her bedroom, paused, then pointed at a gilded icon hanging on the wall.

164

"You see this *iqouneh* (icon) Suad?" she asked excitedly.

"Yes," I replied, staring at Christ's gilded face.

Oh, God. I don't believe this icon has been hanging on this wall for so many years and I never noticed how beautiful it was. Shame on you, Suad. Like typical Russian or Greek icons painted on wood, this one had the shape of a book: yes, a thirty by twenty centimeter metal book, five centimeters thick.

The icon consisted of a florally-decorated gilded sheet in the middle of which were three cuts or openings: one around Christ's head and long hair, another around his left palm in which he held an open bible, and a third around his right hand. The movement of his fingers suggested a cross.

The brown colouring of Christ's head and his two hands contrasted nicely with the gilded background. The halo around the head, the script in the bible and the hems of the wide robe draped over him were all decorated in white, again contrasting beautifully with the gold.

I was totally absorbed in the delicate decorations of the halo around Christ's head when I heard Umm Salim speak again.

"This is an extremely valuable *iqouneh*, Suad. It is made of gilded metal and was given to us as a present by an uncle of Edmon's who lived in Jerusalem, I can't remember his name now."

"But Mother, I thought you didn't take any valuables with you when you left home!"

"True, I didn't. However, a year or two later a Russian nun who claimed to have bought it in Jaffa brought it to me in Beirut, or perhaps in Ramallah. I was happy to re-acquire it. I paid her what she asked for, all the money we had then. I think it was around one hundred and fifty dinars."

Having paid in dinars made me suspect that the Russian nun would have brought it to Umm Salim after she, Edmon and Salim came to live in Ramallah in 1951.

Umm Salim also learnt that her beloved dining table, the Persian carpets given to her by her brother Najib, and other items of her furniture were up for sale as well.

"But at that point we didn't have the money to buy back the rest of our stolen furniture."

Jaffa / Tel Aviv

It must have been in the mid-Nineties.

Shumuel and I were sitting in the back seat chatting in the most polite and over-friendly tones – the fake manner often used by both Palestinians and Israelis when talking to one another in an attempt to hide the exasperation they feel towards each other.

That late evening I was returning to Jerusalem from Tel Aviv where I had participated in a seminar on the prospects of peace between Palestinians and Israelis.

At that time there was still hope.

Shumuel, who sat right next to me, was a rather friendly middle-aged Israeli politician who had apparently also taken part in another seminar at the same conference.

In the same over-friendly tone Shumuel told me that he was at one time a high-ranking Mossad agent (the Israeli intelligence agency). Oh my God, Shumuel Toledano, I gasped, and almost fainted. I trembled to my very core. Shumuel must have sensed it from my glazed eyes, expressionless face and stiffening body.

But no.

He, in exactly the same *friendly* tone, continued to share with me, in Arabic, our *common* history, once he knew we were originally from Jaffa.

"Right after the battle of Jaffa ended in May 1948 the town was totally deserted. Many Palestinians had left their homes. I remember vividly how I, together with other Jewish soldiers, entered one of the Arab houses in al Ajami. On the coffee table

166

in the middle of the living room was a pot of coffee, still warm, that someone must have made that very morning but had to leave behind in a hurry …"

After a long pause he continued: "You know, Suad, as long as I live I shall never forget *that moment.*"

Nor will I.

Through my tightly clenched teeth I tried to take a deep breath to stop the tears from brimming over in my eyes. Immediately, I felt a sourness in my throat.

Although I managed not to cry that afternoon, my tears and my voice always fail me whenever I try to tell that story.

At Umm Salim's house in Ramallah, on the veranda, she and I continued to drink our two cups of coffee as we both gazed out of the window, into the horizon where that other pot of coffee had been left behind.

Never-ending Chapter

My country: As close to me as my prison
– Mahmoud Darwish

Would You ever let go of Me?

Would you *ever* let go of me
For a lifetime
For a year
A month
An hour
A minute
Even a second?

No

If *ever*
If ever we get an apology
If ever we get compensation for our losses
It would not be about a lost country
It would not be about a lost field
Or an orange grove
Or a lost home

No

It would not be about the hundreds of bulldozed villages
Or the scattering of a whole nation
The shattering of a whole society
It would not be about losing a livelihood
A stolen piano, a Persian carpet or a first baby photo-album
And it would not be about someone's personal library
An abandoned Arab horse or a Cypriot donkey
Nor a Persian cat nor even Shasa, the monkey that my mother
    gave me a few days before the war

No

And it would not be about the blossoming almond trees and
    the red flowering pomegranates that were *not* picked
    tenderly in the spring of 1948 nor the following summer
And it would not be about firing at the farmers who returned
    to harvest the fields they had left behind
Nor would it be about the many deserted budding roses
Or a bride's wardrobe and her many cherished wedding gifts
Or a child or an old woman who was forgotten, left behind
    in the chaos

No

It would not be about concealing a crime or falsifying history
It would not be about blaming the victim
It would not be about dehumanisation and stereotyping
It would not be about making new "wandering Jews" out of
    us
It would not be about reversing roles and images

No

If at all
It will *only* be about an *obsession*

Yes, an obsession

My dreams are all about you
And my nightmares are all because of you
My happiness is related to you
And my sadness comes from you
My expectations are all concerning you
And my disappointments pile up beside you

Yes

And if I run away, I run away from you
And if I come back, I come back to you
If I love someone, it is because of what they think of you
And if I hate someone, it is because of what they say about
   you

Yes

And it is because of you:
Nothing in my life is normal
Nothing in my life is neutral
Nothing is mundane
Or even insignificant

And how very exhausting it is

How I desire one ordinary day when you do not haunt me
How I long for a pleasant evening where you are not invited
How I yearn to forget you
How I wish for amnesia or a stroke that
Will neatly remove every trace of you:
Thoughts, memories, emotions
Gone forever

I heard them moan for you before I was born
And I heard them moan for you after I was born and ever
  after
Their bedtime stories are about you
And their daydreaming is also about you
I've seen them cry, laugh, praise and curse

You, you, and only YOU
I had to learn everything about you
I had to imagine you from across a border
Miss you
Love you
Defend you
Cry for you
Write about you
Talk about you
And, in imperative form, love you

And how very exhausting *it is*

Above all I have to keep my sanity with all the brutality
  around you
Every hour every minute and every second
If ever I do come to terms with what has happened to you
I must banish that part of my brain
That cherishes reason, logic and justice

Palestine

Will you ever set us free?